Personally Speaking

Personally Speaking

Walter Carrington on
the F. M. Alexander Technique

in discussion with
Seán Carey

Mouritz

First edition 1986 (Sheildrake Press)
Second, revised and enlarged edition
published May 2001by

Mouritz
6 Ravenslea Road
London SW12 8SB
United Kingdom

www.mouritz.co.uk

ISBN 0–9525574–1–X paperback

A CIP Catalogue record for this book
is available from the British Library.

Design, lay-out and typesetting by Jean M. O. Fischer
Cover pictures by Jean M. O. Fischer

Set in 10.2/12.2 Adobe Garamond
in Aldus PageMaker 6.5

Printed on 80gsm High Opaque
in Great Britain by the Bath Press,
Bath, England

Contents

Preface

The first edition of this book was published in 1986. It has now been out of print for nearly a decade. For this new edition extensive revisions have been made – we have added a considerable amount of new material and taken quite a lot out – in order to make it both more readable and more practically relevant to students and teachers of the Alexander Technique. Most of the new material comes from conversations held between us at the Constructive Teaching Centre in 1994 and 1995. Some additional material gathered in 1999 has also been included.

We would like to express our gratitude to Jean Fischer who made many invaluable comments and suggestions on the original and revised versions of the text and who was, moreover, instrumental in convincing us that a second edition ought to be published. We are also indebted to Paul Gordon for his generous help in checking the manuscript.

Needless to say, the responsibility for the views expressed in this book rests solely with the authors.

Seán Carey
Walter Carrington
London, 2000

Introduction

The Alexander Technique has now more than one hundred years of history behind it, and this book is both a record of some important parts of that history and a contribution to it.

Why should our history be important to us? Isn't it just "bunk", as Henry Ford famously said? As exponents of a method of freeing oneself from accumulated habits, shouldn't we be living in the present, open to the future, not looking back? But every group, from family to nation, has a history, and every individual has a history, a story. Our story helps us to make sense of our lives. We do not prevent the past repeating itself in the future by ignoring it, but by consciously considering it and learning from it.

The originator of the Technique, F. M. Alexander, died in 1955, and very few teachers working today knew him personally. Walter Carrington is a vitally important link to that period from the time FM began a formal programme for training teachers, to the present. He was the person who carried on the original teacher training course after FM's death, and he has himself (and later with his wife, Dilys) been responsible for the training of more Alexander teachers than anyone else.

In preparing the second edition of this book, Seán Carey has removed material from the first edition that is no longer relevant, and has added a considerable amount of new material, much of it dealing with important aspects of teaching the Alexander Technique.

There is significant information here about FM's training course in the 1930s and in the postwar years, and a description of how after FM's death Walter slowly added elements to the training such as the reading of FM's books and the small groups for supervised practical work. Many aspects of teaching are discussed: the evolution and value of chair and table work; the value of the established approach to training; some very interesting insights into the use of the hands in teaching; the importance of lying in semi-supine and how to determine the height of books under the head; the use of monkey, hands on the back of the chair, and the whispered ah; the origins of saddle work; comments on teaching groups; handling difficult pupils; and hints about the elusive subject of directing as a non-verbal process.

Much of this is the distillation of what Walter Carrington learned from FM combined with his own very long teaching experience. Throughout his teaching career he has always maintained a large private practice as well as training teachers, and he has continued to take on new pupils to keep in touch with the realities of the beginner's situation.

Included also are some records of FM's own views that are of great interest. For instance, I do not think anywhere else will you read what FM thought of the practice of lifting a pupil's pelvis on the table. In relation to FM's views, Walter says the following: "Of course when I quote FM on these matters, I'm perfectly aware that he wasn't the Pope and that just because he said something doesn't mean that he was right: I'm prepared to allow for the possibility that he was completely wrong. Indeed in all these matters we've been discussing it's a matter of experiment and trying things out to find out for oneself."

I am sure Walter would want all readers to apply the same attitude to his own views and comments in this book. Of course there is no papal succession and no papal infallibility in the Alexander world. Some readers may not share all the views expressed in this book, but I would urge anyone not to disagree lightly with either FM or Walter, not without carefully considering your reasons and allowing for the possibility that further experience may change your mind. As we move further away from FM's time we will need to have an ongoing dialogue with our own history and traditions. In the development of any art, profession or skill we need to learn from the past, critically appraise it and consider what elements may be purely of their own time, and what are essential to carry forward with us. When the next few generations of Alexander teachers continue that dialogue, this book will give them invaluable material to consider.

John Nicholls
Brighton
March 2001

PART I

Walter, how did you first come into contact with the Alexander Technique?

I first heard about the Technique through my school form-master, W. H. Eynon Smith, whose letter regarding the Technique to the *Times Literary Supplement*, incidentally, is reproduced in *The Universal Constant in Living*. It came about in this way: my mother was an invalid and virtually bedridden, suffering from a condition that had been diagnosed as mucous colitis and visceroptosis: mucous colitis is inflammation of the colon and visceroptosis is the dropping of all the internal organs. These two conditions made the digestion of food practically impossible. Of course, she'd had all the usual tests and examinations, but the doctors didn't seem to know what to try next. One day in 1934 when I was nineteen and on the point of leaving school, I was talking to Eynon Smith, who asked after mother. I gave him a report, and he asked whether I'd ever come across the work of a man called F. Matthias Alexander. He'd read all his books and had always intended to look into it further, but had never got round to it. I think I am right in saying that he had come across the Technique when he read a favourable review of *The Use of the Self* in the *British Medical Journal* of 1932. Anyway I told him that I'd never heard of this man, F. Matthias Alexander, nor his Technique. So Eynon Smith lent me one of FM's books – it was *Man's Supreme Inheritance* as far as I can remember – and it made quite an impression on me. It was certainly different from anything I'd previously come across, and I was so taken by it that I passed it on to my father, who was also very interested by it.

After that I wrote to Ashley Place in Victoria, where FM was teaching, asking for an appointment for mother. She went along to meet FM, who spent quite a long time looking at her and then said yes, he thought he might be able to help her but that she would have to come to him every day for six weeks and then, at the end of that period, he would review the situation. FM's fee at that time was three guineas a lesson, which meant that if she was going to have a lesson every day for six weeks it would be an expensive business. You have to remember that at that time the average typist's wage was something like two pounds fifty a week. Incidentally, FM's scale of fees derived from those charged by Harley Street consultants. When he first came to London, he charged four guineas a lesson, which was the same as a consultant's fee, because, as he explained, his work would only be taken seriously if he put it at that level. Then at some stage – I don't know exactly when – he decided that, since people were coming for a series of lessons rather than one or two consultations, he would reduce his fee to three guineas a lesson, and it remained at that level for the rest of his life.

Anyway, considering that we didn't really know anything about the Technique it was, as I've indicated, quite a big decision. We also had the problem of getting mother from Shepherd's Bush, where we lived, to Victoria and that also meant the expense of a taxi. Finally it was decided that mother would go, and the result was that FM quite literally put her back on her feet. He made an extraordinary change in those few weeks. In fact, mother went on having lessons and had some seventy to eighty lessons with FM over a period of several years. She lived through the blitz and went on until her ninety-second year. For the last twenty years, she was living alone after my father died and managed to look after herself and the house quite successfully. She kept up her practice of the Technique and after the war when I returned from the RAF I gave her weekly lessons.

So it was the transformation that you'd seen in your mother that convinced you that there was something in the Technique?

That's right. Another factor was that Eynon Smith, who'd watched mother's progress, also decided to go to FM for lessons. Eynon Smith was supposed to be a perfectly fit and healthy chap – he'd rowed when he was at Oxford for example – but he did have a typical, old-fashioned rowing chest and FM made a big change there as well. So having seen the changes in both mother and Eynon Smith, I was naturally very interested in the Technique. Indeed, at some point my mother offered to pay for me to have some lessons with FM and I jumped at the chance. I considered myself, like Eynon Smith, to be a perfectly fit and healthy young man – I certainly didn't think there was anything the matter with me – but FM convinced me from the second lesson that I couldn't use either my brain or my body to any good purpose.

He stated that explicitly?

No, I don't think he said it explicitly, but he somehow managed to make it pretty clear that that was his opinion. Then in the course of those early lessons I started to meet some of the newly qualified teachers from the first ever training course, as well as those who were currently training. I began to think that I would like to train as well.

Just returning to the question of Alexander's fees: did he always charge three guineas a lesson? Someone told me that FM once gave some lessons to a carpenter for free.

He certainly gave my mother a large concession on her fees. There was a man from Newcastle-upon-Tyne – his name was Miller – and FM gave him a course of lessons for nothing. But he wasn't a carpenter, he was a plumber.

He'd written to FM saying that he'd read all of his books and found the whole thing very interesting, but how could a working man like himself possibly afford lessons? He considered it all terribly unfair. FM wrote back telling him that if he was ever able to get down to London he would give him some free lessons. He eventually did manage to get down to London and had his lessons. In fact, FM found him an interesting pupil, and when he returned to Newcastle he occasionally wrote to FM on the back of old brown paper bags, which Alexander found very amusing. It also amused Aldous Huxley, who was having lessons at the time, and very often when he came in for a lesson he said to FM: "Well, have you had another letter from Miller yet?" And it was undoubtedly that episode that led Huxley to use the name Miller for the Alexander character in his novel, *Eyeless in Gaza*. In actual fact, "Miller" was a composite character including FM and FM's friend and physician, J. E. R. McDonagh. But going back to the question of fees: yes, FM did make concessions to people occasionally.

Did Alexander insist that everyone come for five lessons a week for six weeks?

He gave my mother five lessons a week for six weeks because of her very serious condition; she was, after all, virtually bedridden. The standard procedure that he followed and expected of us was that pupils should have a lesson five times a week for three or four weeks. He wanted to ensure – we all wanted to ensure – that there were as many successes and as few failures as possible. What we wanted to avoid was the possibility that people would say: "Well I had a few Alexander lessons but they didn't do much good". If people have an intensive introduction to the Technique they certainly learn something. My advice to teachers nowadays is that they follow a similar procedure if they possibly can. Where it's not possible, a teacher should still aim to give a new pupil three lessons a week. Of course, these days we don't have to prove ourselves as much as we used to, so it's not so serious if people have some lessons and then say it didn't do much good; but it's better to avoid that if at all possible. I still remember being astonished when Irene Tasker took some people on for one lesson a week when she was working by herself in South Africa. Until I knew her better and saw the results, I wouldn't have tried it myself; but

I found that there were people who'd definitely learned something on one lesson a week. One has to be open-minded about these things. What I now say to people who for one reason or another find it impossible to come in for more than one lesson a week is: "Well, I'm willing to go ahead and try it, but I must warn you that I don't really have much expectation of success. If it doesn't work out, you've got to remember that it's probably because we haven't really given it a proper chance." I normally ask people to come at least three times a week for three or four weeks, then twice a week for two or three weeks and then carry on with one lesson a week.

But if someone has a difficult journey, then to ask them to come so often may be counterproductive: one does have to consider each case carefully.

Reading the accounts of first-generation teachers like Lulie Westfeldt* and Frank Pierce Jones†, it seems that an important factor in their decision to train as Alexander teachers was a very powerful "aha!" type experience in one or more of their early lessons. Did you have that kind of experience?

I can't say that I did. I can't remember any experiences corresponding to those described by Lulie or Frank, but then I hadn't gone to FM with anything apparently wrong with me. On the other hand, after lessons, I did see sufficient change in myself, combined with the changes I'd witnessed in my mother and Eynon Smith, to make me realise that things were happening. It was this overall experience that made me want to train.

Before I left school I had become a Roman Catholic and thought that I might become a Jesuit. Father Martindale, who was a well known Jesuit of the time, had received me into the church and obtained a dispensation for me to go as a novice. However, it had also been thought that I might go up to Oxford and read history or something. In those days, you have to remem-

---

* Lulie Westfeldt *F. Matthias Alexander: The Man and His Work* (1998).
† Frank Pierce Jones *Freedom to Change* (1997).

ber, if you were able to pay the fees there wasn't much of a problem in getting into university. It was undoubtedly easier if you knew someone in one of the colleges who was prepared to recommend you. My father was a vicar, and the Bishop of London knew me and had expressed his willingness to recommend me and, of course, he had some scholarships in his gift.

What was the attitude of your family and friends to your decision to join the Alexander training course? Did they, for example, think it an odd sort of profession to take up?

My father said: "Look, either you can go to university or you can do the training course, but you can't do both because we can't afford it." So there were choices to be made. My father was a tolerant, broadminded person and had taken my conversion to Catholicism very well – I think he rather sympathised with my desire to join the Jesuits. My mother, on the other hand, was horrified, and thought that going to study the Alexander Technique was an excellent idea. So that summed up the family attitude and there really was no one else concerned, apart from Eynon Smith, who agreed with my mother and was himself much in favour of the Technique. Thus I didn't have any opposition – when I decided to join the training course. However, by the time I had finished and gained my teaching certificate World War II had broken out and the future for everyone looked very uncertain; military service was inevitable, I had been in the OTC at school and did not find the prospect of Army life very attractive, so I volunteered for flying training in the Royal Air Force and eventually qualified as a pilot.

There are two other aspects to the story that I should tell you. After my mother had been having lessons for some time, Alexander and his students decided to stage a production of *Hamlet* at the Old Vic. My mother and I went to the play, and that, in fact, was the first time I actually saw Alexander – on stage playing *Hamlet*. People have often asked me what it was like; was it a good production and so on? But quite honestly I can't remember. I am sure that it wasn't a bad production because if it had been awful I would have remembered. At the age of nineteen you're always pretty critical of your parents' enthusiasms. Reports at the time – in the press and so on – suggested that it was pretty good.

The second part of the story is this: one day when my mother was having a lesson with FM they got talking about me and so Alexander invited me to dinner.

He'd obviously been interested in what mother had told him about me and was probably on the lookout for young people who he thought might like to train as teachers. You must remember that at that time the work wasn't very widely known, and he was after recruits. So I went to Ashley Place about six-thirty one September evening. Alexander opened the door, and that was the first time I met him face to face. We had a glass of sherry in the sitting room which, as I later discovered, doubled up as the students' room, and then we went out for dinner to the Café Royal, which was one of FM's favourite haunts. We had our meal in the restaurant at the top of the building, and the only thing I remember about the occasion was that Alexander didn't have much small-talk – though it was clear he was very interested in horse-racing, a subject which I didn't know the first thing about, so that was a bit of a non-starter. I was also surprised when the conversation turned to astrology and I discovered that FM was a reader of newspaper horoscopes. Some years previously I had become interested in astrology and I'd even gone as far as to teach myself trigonometry so that I could do all the calculations; so I was appalled to find that a man of his intelligence would have any truck with the sort of astrology found in newspapers.

Did FM believe them?

Oh no. I just think he found them quite amusing, that's all. But I was surprised that such a serious man would engage in such a frivolous pursuit. Anyway, after dinner FM suggested that we might as well walk back to Ashley Place. As we were coming into Piccadilly, we bumped into his solicitor – a nice chap called Barraclough, who was quite a character – but afterwards I remember FM solemnly telling me that solicitors and accountants were the worst sort of people to have as Alexander pupils and, in my experience, he was pretty right. There've been a few shining exceptions, of course, but not many.

There's something about the way they think, is there?

Yes, and their overall attitude. They tend to be out of touch with their bodies. They spend so much of their time thinking about abstract situations, they lose awareness of their surroundings. But funnily enough, as FM said, that characteristic doesn't apply to barristers: it seems that the Bar is quite different from the Law Society. Anyway, after we'd said farewell to Barraclough, we caught a taxi and returned to Ashley Place and had a glass of port. FM smoked a cigar and I had one or two of his cigarettes, and that was the end of the evening. On my way out FM said that if I wanted some lessons he'd give me some. So that was arranged and, as I've said, that eventually led me to join the training course.

What sort of people trained in those days: were they avant-garde types, for example?

They were a very mixed bunch really. I wouldn't describe any of them as particularly avant-garde. The first person to register for the training course was Marjorie Barstow who came from Lincoln, Nebraska. She'd done ballet training in America and had read about the Technique after her ballet teacher had recommended it. She came from quite a wealthy family, and on a visit to London decided that she'd find out what the Technique was all about. She had some lessons from FM and was so impressed that she decided there and then to sign up for the training course that he was proposing. Then there was Patrick Macdonald: he was the third son of Peter Macdonald, a Yorkshire doctor. Pat had been looked upon as rather weak and sub-standard from a general health point of view from the age of eleven, so his father and mother thought that it would be good for him to train. He'd got a history degree and a half-blue at Cambridge, but the only thing he was really interested in was boxing. I suppose you could say that was a bit avant-garde but, honestly, I think his decision to train also reflected the fact that he didn't really have any other particular career in mind.

George Trevelyan was the son of Charles Trevelyan, the Minister of Education in the first Labour government. George had done an apprenticeship in cabinet-making after his degree at university but, like Pat and me, I don't think he knew what he wanted to do, and again the family was keen on the Technique. I don't know how Gurney MacInnes got in but I think that he too was a young man who hadn't decided what to do in life. Then there was Erika Schumann (Whittaker) who was Ethel Webb's niece – Ethel was FM's secretary. Erika's father had served in the German army and she, along with many other people who had German connections, were having a hard time of it in that period. Irene Stewart and Margaret Goldie had both signed up through a connection with Miss E. E. Lawrence of the Froebel Institute. Charles Neal came in at a slightly later date than the others: he joined because he suffered from appalling asthma and it was thought that he needed more work than he could get just from having private lessons and that if he learned to teach, that would be an added bonus.

So overall the people who decided to train were a young group of individuals who had various reasons for coming in, though I don't honestly think that anyone had any vision of becoming a professional Alexander teacher. They weren't really motivated in that way.

I came in at a later stage. When I joined, Max Alexander and Marjory Mechin (now Barlow) – who were FM's nephew and niece respectively (Max was A. R. Alexander's son) – were just finishing their training.

The September intake of 1936 included me, Eric de Peyer, Elizabeth Faulkner, who'd worked at the "little school" at Penhill, Margaret Lumsden, who'd come from Australia, and Peggs Dunlop, who, by an extraordinary coincidence was the sister of a chap who'd been a good friend of mine at school. Peggs was a severe epileptic and had quite a lot of fits during the three years of training, but the work helped her enormously. So there were five of us on the training course.

Why did Alexander set up a training course at all?

I certainly don't think he did it for financial reward; rather, he realised that the demand for teachers would gradually increase. I suspect he was very influenced by the success of Irene Tasker's work at the "little school" at Penhill. Moreover, it's clear from his writings that FM was very concerned with children's development, so there obviously had to be enough teachers to meet any expected demand from that direction.

Did he give up some of his ordinary teaching to make time for the training course?

Yes, he did. He was always fully booked.

What was the training like in those days?

As far as I can make out and from what people have told me, there were all sorts of problems on the first training course, largely because, as FM himself later admitted, he didn't have any experience of training students. Further, he wasn't a man to have preconceived ideas on the subject and his approach was therefore experimental. He'd written *The Use of the Self* to set out his experiences as clearly as possible, and he genuinely thought that with that text as a blueprint and the fact that he'd be on hand to answer any queries, the students would be able to work it all out for themselves. He really thought this arrangement would work perfectly. With the benefit of hindsight, it's obvious that FM thought that the students would be like himself – committed to self-help and self-enquiry.

Everyone was apparently happy and cheerful for the first term, but by the end of that time FM was beginning to get very disenchanted. He couldn't see any signs that the students were beginning to apply themselves and grapple with the problems. Instead, as he put it: "All they were doing was going around imitating me like a cartload of monkeys!" He had a very poor opinion of imitation as a way of learning, and you can imagine that he was disgusted with the state of affairs! Of course, the students' point of view was radically different and has been well put by Lulie Westfeldt in her book.* It's very understandable: the students had joined the training course fully expecting that they were going to be taught to teach. The idea that they had to figure it all out for themselves never occurred to them. They were expecting something to happen, and when it didn't they became increasingly bored and disenchanted.

Moreover, they couldn't understand why FM, who had seemed very welcoming and cheerful to begin with, was beginning to look increasingly sour. So overall things weren't satisfactory from anyone's point of view. At this point FM got a brilliant idea: he remembered that before he left Sydney to come to London in 1904 he'd had a group of young people around him – they were aspiring young actors and the work was very much voice-oriented – who'd given a few public performances of *Hamlet* and *The Merchant of Venice*. In fact, they'd gone successfully on tour, and audiences had been amazed at what raw, inexperienced actors could do on the basis of the new teaching. So now in London FM thought the best thing to do with the students was to get them to do one of the plays, *The Merchant of Venice*. They learned the various parts in accordance with the principles of the Technique, Alexander considered this the best possible way to get them to grapple with their practical problems. Indeed, to a considerable extent he was proved right. Although most of them didn't like it and didn't really see the point of it at all – as Lulie Westfeldt said, she'd gone to learn to become an Alexander teacher, not an actor – the production was surprisingly successful. It was later decided that they'd put on *Hamlet* in the second year, and in the third year they did a sort of concert recital with some singing, piano-playing and scenes from the two plays. So that was the main activity of the first training course and there's no doubt that, at the end of three years, they'd greatly improved their use of themselves, even if they had little or no idea about teaching the Technique.

---

* Lulie Westfeldt *F. Matthias Alexander: The Man and His Work* (1998).

You mentioned that in the early days of FM's teaching the Technique was very much voice-oriented. When did he develop the use of his hands?

I'm certain he was using his hands from the very beginning. A group of people came to him after his last public recital in Auckland, New Zealand, and asked if he would give them lessons in voice. That was understandable, because the local papers had dubbed FM "The Breathing Man", and people assumed the Technique had something to do with breath control and voice production. He described his discoveries to the group: how he had stiffened his neck, pulled his head back, raised his chest and so on. While he was explaining this to them, he was using his hands to get it across. After all, if someone says: "What do you mean by pulling down under the chin and pulling your head back?", you would naturally show them, wouldn't you? So he was using his hands in those early days and did so increasingly as time went on. In fact, I remember him telling me the story of working on a woman in Australia who had a very fixed ribcage after having contracted TB. When he looked back on that episode in the light of what he subsequently knew, he was horrified to think what he'd tried to do in an effort to free her ribs. He was obviously making some sort of positive effort to get the ribs to move – performing a definite manipulation, if you like. But my overall impression is that it wasn't until quite late in his life that FM really appreciated the tremendous importance of the skill he'd developed with this hands.

He thought rather optimistically that if you could explain the logic of the situation to someone in a simple and straightforward way – if you could put it to them rationally – then, unless they were stupid or had some ulterior motive, they would understand. Of course, as he was explaining things to people he was busy using his hands and, as I said, it was only gradually that he began to find more and more that it was what he did with his hands that counted. As long as he made the right kind of soothing noises, it didn't seem to matter very much what he said. Towards the end of his life, although he was still making simple, rational statements, he no longer expected people to be able to change things just by listening to him.

It seems that on the first training course FM would occasionally come over and put his hands over the students' hands and the energy would flow through and things would happen, so a certain amount of "hands-on" work was going on, but not really an awful lot. In any case, most of that took place in the fourth year – the additional year of the first training course – when FM decided that after three years the students were nowhere near ready to go out and teach.

That's one part of the story. The other part concerns the efforts of Pat Macdonald, who was getting very bored indeed with the way things were going. Alexander used to give the students a class in the morning; then at lunchtime they all went to the nearest pub, where they had something to eat and drink, before returning to Ashley Place and lying down on the floor of the students' room. Macdonald decided that this routine was leading nowhere and they'd better get on and work something out for themselves. Alexander had found that it was necessary for his head to go forward and up, and so, in teaching, what you had to do, presumably, was to take people's heads forward and up, and your own head forward and up into the bargain. Macdonald started working with some of the students on this principle and they experimented with the use of their hands and taking each other up.

There was, however, another group of students who considered that all this experimentation was quite wrong, because FM said that you weren't supposed to do anything and so all this "doing" must be contrary to principle. Some of this latter group went to FM and complained, particularly because Pat was being encouraged in his endeavours by FM's brother, A. R. Alexander. Although the two brothers had a deep and understanding relationship, there was also a bit of friction between them, and some people used to delight in trying to set AR and FM against one another.

By the time I met them, the students were split into two groups. One group was using their hands, but totally ineffectively, so that from my point of view it was a waste of time getting them to work on you, because they just pawed you about. The other group – Pat Macdonald's lot – seemed to have some idea about things, and my experience at the time was that you felt you were getting somewhere with them.

Did FM either oppose or endorse these groups at any time?

No, he stood apart. You see, it wasn't his style to get mixed up in these matters. If anyone went to him and complained, he would nod rather noncommittally and that would be it. Anyway, by the time I came onto the training course in September 1936, a lot of the teachers from that training course had scattered. Pat Macdonald, for example, was based in Birmingham in an effort to establish a centre outside London and only appeared intermittently; Margaret Goldie spent a lot of her time at the "little school" at Penhill near Bexley, Kent; Max Alexander was due to go with his father to Boston; Marjory Barlow was only doing a bit of teaching and was looked upon by her uncle, FM, as pretty much a dogsbody to run his errands; George Trevelyan only appeared occasionally and was trying to build up a practice from his flat in Victoria, but that wasn't very successful; Gurney MacInnes had an appointment as an Alexander teacher at a small public school called Weymouth College – a quite successful experiment but which came to an abrupt halt with the outbreak of World War II; Jean MacInnes was working in the medical practice of Mungo Douglas, one of FM's doctor supporters, in Bolton, but she didn't really have enough experience for that; Marjorie Barstow had gone back to the USA after three years; Lulie Westfeldt also went back to America; Kitty Merrick had had a second nervous breakdown and had entered a nursing home, although she later recovered and went on to become an Alexander teacher.

When I started on the training course, we usually had a class with Alexander in the afternoon. Generally the routine was as follows: at the appointed time we all assembled in the teaching room at Ashley Place and took a place with a chair or a stool. Then FM came in – he was normally punctual – and worked on each person in turn – taking them in and out of the chair, putting them into "monkey" and doing whispered "ah"s. He gave everyone the same amount of time, so the length of a turn depended on the number of people in the room. If there were any junior teachers around, they followed FM and worked on the students. At the end of an hour or so, that was it for the day. I should also say that, as FM made the rounds, there was often conversation about almost anything. In fact, people used to start conversations to relieve the monotony. Sometimes, as FM was giving turns, something relevant to the Technique would crop up and he then would give a demonstration or explanation. In those days, there was no question of anybody putting their hands on anybody else.

The general thinking was that one shouldn't expect to put hands on until one had done a couple of years' training, so what most students did was to go into "monkey" and practise putting hands on the backs of chairs, doing whispered "ah"s, lying down and so on. I know I didn't put my hands on anyone until a couple of years had gone by. I think I'm right in saying that it was Pat Macdonald who gave me an introduction to "hands on". He used to sit in a chair while I put my hands on his head, then he told me what I was doing wrong.

So, even on your course, Alexander still wasn't giving you much information about the use of the hands?

No, he didn't teach very much about the hands in any formal way. I think he thought that if we watched him working every day, we would work it out for ourselves, because it was being demonstrated every day.

Did he still come over and put his hands over yours?

Yes, he did. And he nearly always said, "You're stiffening the wrists. That's no good. You can't do anything if your wrists are stiff!" But having told you you were stiffening the wrists, he didn't then go on to tell you how not to stiffen them.

He identified the problem without offering a solution, in other words?

As far as we were concerned, yes. We'd go round giving the hand a good shake which, of course, doesn't do any good at all. You see, on the one hand, Alexander had never had much experience of training students and, on the other, he himself hadn't been taught by anyone else how to use his hands – he'd worked it out for himself – so his standpoint was quite different from ours. From his point of view, he didn't understand what students needed in the way of help. Also, I think there were certain things about the process that were so obvious to him and he felt he'd demonstrated them over and over again. And, as far as he was concerned, these were very simple, straightforward things.

So were you happy on the training course?

Yes, I was. I had a strong impression that the junior teachers were learning rapidly. I thought that Pat Macdonald was an extremely good teacher and was finding out about things; Marjory Barlow also. I didn't much admire what some of the other teachers were doing, but I thought that things would eventually work out for them. In addition, lots of very exciting things were happening in those years apart from the actual work on the training course. For example, it was the time when nineteen doctors got together and signed a declaration of faith in the Technique, which was published in the *British Medical Journal*; George Bernard Shaw was coming for lessons, and so too was Aldous Huxley, who had just published *Eyeless in Gaza* and was preparing *Ends and Means*.

I also became interested in a book called *The Biology of Human Conflict* by Trigant Burrow, because it was felt at the time that this was plagiarising some of FM's work. Indeed, I wrote to Burrow and obtained what we took as admissions that he had "borrowed" from FM. It was also the time when, through Alma Frank, who joined the training course in 1937, George Coghill became interested in the Technique. I began a study of Coghill's and Alexander's work, which kept me very busy indeed for most of the following year. The project involved reading all of Coghill's publications and re-reading FM's books very carefully on a comparative basis. It was hard work but very rewarding, and I finished the paper in 1940, just before I went into the Air Force. It was a comparative study of the two men: FM working at a very practical level with human beings and Coghill performing some complex, laboratory analysis of reflex patterns in animals. You have to remember that in those days the amount of scientific information relevant to the Technique was really very small. There had been a few articles and references by Peter Macdonald, Pat Macdonald's father, published in *The Lancet*, Anthony Ludovici's book, *Health and Education through Self-Mastery*, and that was about it.

Alexander read your piece?

Yes, he was delighted with it and initially wanted to use some of it in *The Universal Constant in Living*. Then, on reflection, he thought he would deal with the whole issue in a separate work but, alas, nothing ever came of that because after the war we were plunged into the libel-action and we all had other things to think of.

How do you evaluate your work now?

Well, I think it stands the test of time. There was nothing I wanted to alter or revise when it was published.* I don't particularly like the title but I've never been able to come up with a better one.

Overall would you go along with Lulie Westfeldt's claim that FM was a great pioneer but a poor teacher?

Yes, I'd say that was a fair comment. On the other hand, the obvious question, given the novelty of the situation both for FM and the students, is: could anyone else have done any better at that point? I think we're much better at it now because we've learned a great deal over the years.

---

* Walter H. M. Carrington *The Foundations of Human Well-Being* (1994).

I've heard from a number of people that Alexander didn't really appreciate the difficulties that people encountered in learning the Technique.

I think that's true. A self-taught person – an autodidact – is always likely to be a poor teacher, because anything one has worked out for oneself is different from anything learned from somebody else. This automatically leads to difficulties in teaching and explanation. Indeed, over the years some people blamed FM's teaching abilities – or lack of them – for their failure to understand the Technique. The most amusing case that comes to mind – at least it amused us at the time – was that of an Australian chap who joined the training course in 1946 or 1947 and couldn't understand it at all. He said he was sure that FM had a secret he was perhaps willing to disclose to a few, but not to the masses, and certainly not to him. He really thought he was being excluded, and eventually packed the course in after two years and went back to Australia.

How did the training of teachers evolve in the period of your contact with FM? When, for example, did he move away from teaching the Technique through performances of *Hamlet* and *The Merchant of Venice*?

By the time I joined the training course, he'd given up all thoughts of people doing plays. All that had finished. But in any case, between 1936 and 1939, he – indeed all of us – became affected by the imminence of war, and that uncertainty made any sort of planning extremely difficult. One couldn't really plan much for the future when one didn't know what the future would hold.

When FM resumed the training course in 1945, he had several teachers assisting who worked with the students outside the main class. This provided more structure to the training. Then, in December 1947, while we were on our Christmas holidays, FM suffered a stroke and for a while wasn't working at all. The training was left to Pat and the rest of us. In September 1948, when he had recovered sufficiently, the rather large group of twenty or so students was split into two. In the morning one group went to Evelyn Mansions, where FM was living at the time, while we took the others at Ashley Place. Then, in the afternoon, this was reversed. Although the students found these arrangements satisfactory, it meant that we – the assistant teachers – didn't have much contact with Alexander for quite a time.

In any case, there still was not much emphasis on using the hands until it was felt that the students had reached a reasonable level of use, which meant, in practice, after about two years. Incidentally, FM was still keen that people should work out the Technique for themselves. Moreover, because he wasn't available for a time after his stroke, he decided that those who had begun the course in 1945 should do another year. He told them all to go off separately from the main training course and work on each other with no help from the assistant teachers. As you can imagine, that wasn't very popular, but a group of them were given certificates in 1949. I remember that FM was a bit shocked by the behaviour of one of the group. He thought that after qualifying they would continue to work at Ashley Place as assistant teachers and, in that way, get more experience. When Alan Murray went off to Australia two or three weeks after qualifying, FM was somewhat surprised, to say the least.

In later years – that is to say in 1954 and 1955 – FM did much less work on the training course. I was teaching in Oxford from 1948 onwards, but in 1952 I received a letter from FM asking me to spend more time at Ashley Place working on the training course, and naturally I agreed. Work on the training course in that period went on in the normal way – people had turns, and after a time began to use their hands – but the first significant change in training came about after FM's death in 1955. While he was alive, the training was his ultimate responsibility and I didn't do anything on the course without first asking his permission: what went on was up to him.

But then after his death I felt that the training course was my responsibility. At that time I was assisted by Peggy Williams and Peter Scott; John Skinner and Irene Stewart also came in sometimes and worked with the students. The first change in training came about because I realised that the students needed more motivation. When FM was around he automatically provided a degree of motivation, not least because he was the originator of and authority on the Technique. After his death, I considered it was important for the students to familiarise themselves with his writings. Thus two or three times a week they sat in a circle and took it in turn to read from the books. While this was going on, the other teachers and I worked on the students and tried to ensure that whilst they were reading they were letting their heads go forward and up, not interfering with their breathing, and so on. This procedure conveniently combined working with the voice and reading the texts.

I soon discovered, however, that this wasn't going to work out because of the immense difficulties most of them had in reading aloud and which tended to block out any awareness of the content of the readings. I then decided to read the books myself in daily half-hour sessions, providing a commentary as we went along and giving the students an opportunity to ask questions. We soon discovered that we ought to look at the writings of other people that had a bearing on the Technique. Thus the daily lecture that we have today emerged.

The second development occurred when I decided to give all the students a private lesson so that I could get to know them and provide them with an opportunity to ask questions outside the group context. FM had given the students private lessons only sporadically, although I must say that when he did so he was very generous with his time. But I formalised it to ensure that everyone regularly got a private lesson.

Another development was my division of the class into groups of three that were then given a specific procedure to work on. I took one group away from the class whilst the assistants worked with the others. Incidentally, I've found that three seems to be the optimum number for a group in this type of work. Nowadays, at the start of the afternoon session, I demonstrate something simple like walking, taking a step, or lifting a telephone directory, and then get the class to work in groups of three once again under the supervision of the teachers. Because of the way the timetable is structured this means that everyone is doing the same thing. We call this afternoon procedure "games" because I realised very early on that people ought to approach this part of the proceedings in a non-endgaining way. No one, for example, is expected to do it "right" or necessarily perform very well. It's not intended to be seen as a formal "exercise" in any sense.

Finally, there was the problem of teaching people how to use their hands. The old tradition from FM's time of students waiting two or three years before they began to learn how to take heads or whatever created a highly charged situation and was likely to be a hit-and-miss affair. I found it unsatisfactory, but recalled that FM continually emphasised that putting the hands on the back of a chair was an essential procedure for giving people the necessary preliminary experience for putting hands on people's shoulders, backs, heads, etc. Another component in all this was to impress upon the students that using their hands in a small group situation is very different from actual teaching – i.e., we were not concerned to teach the student directly how to give a lesson and work on a pupil. I have always been careful to emphasise that the process we are involved in was deliberately artificial, and structured in a way that is not really appropriate to learning how to give an ordinary lesson. But by following this artificial procedure, the student is in a non-endgaining situation where the focus is on him or herself and the interests of the "pupil" are not a major concern. Students are, after all, working on a fellow student who is also carefully looking after him or herself. This emphasis avoids these procedures from the old days when there would be comments like: "You're pulling my head back" – "Your front hand is too stiff"; and so on. Essentially, the new procedure took the negative pressure out of the situation: the students didn't have to be concerned with the problem of "getting it right". In fact, by looking after themselves, the students build up habits of using their hands in such a way that when they come face to face with a real pupil they can then afford to focus their attention on the pupil's requirements because they can be confident that their own conditions will remain satisfactory.

Earlier, you mentioned that Alexander constantly highlighted the problem of stiffening the wrists when putting the hands on without offering much by way of a solution. What solution – if any – do you offer to the students?

One very effective way is to get down into creeping* and in that way you're using the hands as feet – getting the hyperextension and so on. Another way is simply to pay attention to the messages you are sending that are actually causing the wrists to stiffen. You've got to stop sending messages to the flexors to contract and send messages to the extensors to get them to work. Now, because of habit and so forth you'll probably have to send messages for some time before it actually happens. And I think where students and teachers get confused is that instead of inhibiting and directing to get a new situation, they get impatient and try and force it. Further, people often stiffen the wrists because they put their hands on with the intention of doing something rather than to feel what's going on in the other person.

Are there any other common errors in the use of the hands in teaching?

Yes, stiffening the fingers and thumb is a big problem. In fact, some people have very weak and hyper-mobile thumbs. Overall you want the hands to be free and supple. When Alexander put his hands on you, it really felt as if he was enfolding you. There was no sense of gripping or tightening or anything like that. His hands had a quality of openness which meant he was able to get the maximum amount of contact possible. And, of course, the more you can bring the whole hand into contact, the more you can feel and the more purposeful everything is.

Can you give an example?

---

* Moving on the hands and knees with the body prone like a child does.

Yes. Suppose you want to encourage a widening between the pupil's shoulder blades or something like that; then, if you can put an expanding hand on where you want the widening, it stimulates the area in a way that a contracting hand won't. That's really what it's about.

How specific a skill do you think the use of the hands in teaching the Alexander Technique is compared to other ways of using the hands, say, taking hold of a musical instrument, cooking utensils or even (because I was discussing it with someone the other day) a dental drill?

All of the things you mention have specific elements in them – you're using the hands in particular ways to meet certain demands and requirements. But the most important element in the way we use the hands in teaching is to be able to feel what's happening in the pupil in order to diagnose the situation. In the Technique, we're primarily dealing with living tissue whereas even in something like using a dental drill you're dealing with tissue at one stage removed. At a superficial level, people have often tried to compare what we do with sculpting but, once again, the big difference is that a sculptor works on a dead piece of stone or clay and we're working with living tissue. It's a very big difference.

Perhaps the nearest equivalent is found in the realm of horsemanship. It's said that an experienced rider takes hold of the reins as if they were holding a sponge that is fairly full of water. Now, the rider doesn't want to spill the water, but, at the same time, he's just squeezing it and letting it go, squeezing it and letting it go. In other words, the rider is carrying the reins in a very lively manner. And, with that degree of life and mobility in the hand, the rider can feel the horse's mouth and, equally, the horse's mouth can feel the rider's hands. But even in this case, despite the sensitivity with which the rider uses the hands, you still don't have the opening out and extension of the hands that is the hallmark of the Alexander Technique.

Alexander always maintained a private practice at the same time as he ran a training course. Did he consider it important to keep in contact with the general public?

I don't know if FM thought about that very much. There were always people calling in and writing to Ashley Place asking for lessons; old pupils kept coming back and others were recommending their friends, so there was a constant demand for his services. By the time FM was well over eighty years of age, however, we had to say to people: "Look, it's not possible to have all your lessons from FM. If you want a course of lessons, you'll have to have some from the assistant teachers."

But he was still giving about eight lessons a day right up until the day he died. I don't honestly think he thought to do otherwise.

But do you prefer to run a private practice in conjunction with the training course?

I've always said that it's a good idea to do both. I see the two activities as complementary.

In what sense?

Well, on the training course, people get very much more work and get much more experience. In short, they're easier to work on. You get a clearer picture of what people could be like if they didn't interfere and pull themselves down so much. Now, the relevance of this to private teaching is that it provides you with some standard – some criterion – of what you're working for. On the other hand, taking private pupils is really very valuable because it keeps you in touch with what the problems in the real world are.

Was there any evolution in the way FM taught his private pupils?

I certainly observed many fairly subtle changes in his styles of teaching over the years. In fact, it was changing all the time. A major change was imposed on him after his stroke, when he no longer possessed his former strength. Although other teachers might dispute this, I've always maintained that the quality of his teaching improved quite remarkably. You see, he had to give more attention to thought and direction.

Presumably that means that FM was doing his best work in the period just before he died?

Yes, I think so. And one reason I think so is that before he died he was taking several heavy and difficult pupils – people who were overweight, pulled down and limited in movement. I used to watch him teaching, and was surprised to see how easily he handled them and got what he wanted. Then, after he died, I found myself giving lessons to a number of the same people and discovered that I couldn't even begin to approach what I'd seen FM do. That experience brought home to me the quality of his work in a very direct and practical way.

Another point worth recording here is that one of FM's great skills as a teacher was his ability to work with someone in, say, getting in and out of the chair. He gave them just the right amount of stimulus for everything to work, provided that the pupil did their bit in terms of inhibition and direction. If the pupil didn't co-operate in this way it wouldn't work. He was thus able to get people really inhibiting and directing much more effectively than other teachers did – and still do for that matter – who gave the pupil far more support and help than they actually required.

So would the pupil learn much more with FM's minimalist approach?

Yes, they would. But it's a complex business and so much depends on the individual. Clearly if someone is nervous and has a poor opinion of themselves, they feel that it's beyond them and need a lot more encouragement from the teacher. A lot of people go around with an expectation of failure and they rather enjoy a teacher pointing out that it's gone wrong again. That satisfies them as it fits in with their expectations. They're delighted to say to

25

themselves: "Yes, I've failed again". It makes them happy in a perverse sort of way.

Was Alexander working right up until the time he died?

He was working on Friday afternoon, and on Saturday went to the races at Alexandra Palace with John Skinner. This was his usual pattern for a weekend if there was a race meeting being held in or around London. Apparently FM and John had an enjoyable day, although it was very cold. FM had taken up his normal position in the grandstand, where he could see both the races and the bookies on the rails. John placed his bets for him.

After the meeting, they came back to town and had dinner at a restaurant. The story I've always been told is that FM had lobster, a dish he was very fond of but which, because it was so rich, was likely to give him indigestion. Indeed, the next day he wasn't at all well: he put it down to a combination of indigestion and a slight chill and decided to stay in bed. Then on Monday his doctor, J. E. R. McDonagh, was called in and later sent one of his assistants to give FM a few injections. I also remember that on the following Thursday McDonagh came into Ashley Place and said to us: "Look, he's pulling round and getting over it slowly, but he's simply working far too hard and you've got to make sure that he does less." But we knew that FM wouldn't take any notice of us – he did what he wanted to do – so we said to McDonagh: "You tell him!" McDonagh said he thought that everything would be all right, but warned that the next time it might not be so good.

Then, on the following Saturday, FM sent a message over to Ashley Place that he wanted John to fix up his radio so that he could listen to it. He also wanted copies of the day's racing papers so he could study the form. We all naturally thought he was on the mend, although by now he'd been in bed for a week and Margaret Goldie had arranged for a nurse to look after him. On the following Monday morning the nurse was in FM's room tidying up while FM was sitting up and chatting to her.

Then suddenly he simply put his head back on the pillow and he'd gone. The nurse phoned through to Ashley Place to tell us that he'd died and that was that. His heart had undoubtedly gone. This was the tenth of October, 1955; he'd been 86 the previous January.

What was the effect of Alexander's death on your group?

Well, McDonagh had given us warning that FM was likely to die at any time, so we were prepared for it, but it was still a shock. Our immediate reaction was to carry on as usual, and we made no alteration in our routine. In any case, FM hadn't been into the training course for quite a while and things had been going on without him. We had to make some arrangements so that FM's pupils could carry on having lessons, but that was a relatively minor matter.

But wasn't there a sense of loss: after all, FM was the pioneer and, as you mentioned earlier, the authority on the Technique?

We didn't think about it like that: we simply carried on. It was a question of living in the present. The funeral arrangements were made by Margaret Goldie as far as I recall.

I'd be very interested to know how some of the procedures that we now work with evolved: for example, where did Alexander get the idea of using a chair?

I don't know, but my guess is that it was fairly early in his career – I'm talking about 1895 or 1896 – because he wanted the format of a lesson to resemble as closely as possible people's everyday activities. He'd worked out that one of the most universal things people did was to sit and stand – but these are activities that people, almost without exception, do rather badly. He used to make a point of saying to new pupils, "I haven't got anything for you to go away and practice – I can't give you any exercises or anything like that – but here is something you can put into practice right away". He saw it as something anyone could do as soon as they

27

left the teaching room and went and sat on the bus, train or park bench.

Yes, I can see that. But it still leaves unanswered why Alexander chose to use the chair rather than demonstrating the Technique using his original problem situation, namely, the use of the voice.

Well, that's a good point. But he knew from experience that you'd got to do quite a lot of work on people and their general co-ordination – there's a lot for them to understand about inhibition and direction – before they're ready to start voice work.

So the chair provides people with a stimulus which is not too complex relative to vocal work?

Absolutely. The chair has tremendous advantages over lots of other activities. And, in western countries, nearly everyone does a lot of sitting. Of course, in teaching if you just use a chair without reference to other forms of sitting and expect people to make the connection for themselves, you may well be disappointed. You've got to show people how badly they sit not only, say, at a desk but at the theatre and cinema and in a car and aeroplane. Pupils need to have some understanding of the problems in sitting: they nearly always use themselves in such a way that they collapse rather than getting the natural reflexes to work.

What about table work?

Again, I'm not sure exactly when FM started to lie people down but I know that he used a couch – the ordinary day-bed type – and that he used to get his assistants to work with people on that. His sister, Amy, was one of his earliest assistants; she came to England in 1909. Later on he was helped by Ethel Webb and Irene Tasker. He got the assistants to give pupils what he termed "inhibition work". This involved putting the pupil on the couch and the assistant saying: "Now I'm going to move your arm (or your leg); you're to say 'no', while you give your directions to allow me to move it without your interfering with it".

By the time I got involved in the Technique, FM had a couch in the back room of Ashley Place where people would lie down. But most people who had "lying down" work had it on the floor. They lay on a rug with a pile of books under the head and the assistant teachers worked with them, taking them up and down from the floor. The first table was introduced only in 1939, and that came about because we were doing a lot of "lying down" work. It seemed sensible to put pupils on the table rather than scrabble about on the floor. It proved very successful, so after the war we got more built; gradually working on the table came to be regarded as standard practice for everyone except FM. He never put people down himself but called on one of the assistant teachers to do that part of the work. He'd say to us: "Take Mr or Mrs X and put them down and give me a call when you've done so". Then he'd come along, have a look and perhaps do some work with them taking the head and legs – especially the legs. Of course, he showed us how he wanted the table work to be carried out but since we were doing it ourselves we gradually developed our own methods.

So overall table work was developed more by the assistant teachers than by FM?

Yes, that's right. But he was always insistent that when you put people on the table, there must be a good number of books under their heads.

Why did he insist on a good number of books?

Well, I think it's something verifiable by experiment. If there is only a very small number of books relative to the shape of the person's back and overall configuration, it means that the head is thrown back relative to the spine. If someone's lying down in that way, it's not very helpful. If, on the other hand, there are more books under the head, then the head goes more forward. Now, it may go more forward than you actually need it, but it won't really do any harm unless it occurs to a degree where it's really causing pressure on the front of the throat and larynx. But then people will find it uncomfortable anyway and they're not likely to do it.

The main consideration from a practical, teaching point of view is that I like to be able to put my hands on someone's head when they're lying down and find that as I touch the head without doing anything, I can feel the elasticity – the head isn't fixed or stiff – and it's ready to lengthen out under my hands. I don't have to lift it to take it forward before taking it out – it's going forward already. The right thing is doing itself.

The other thing I should emphasise is that FM was very much against performing any sort of manoeuvre with the pelvis. I very well remember on one occasion when we – the assistant teachers – had come up with this brilliant idea that when you'd laid somebody down and got the right thickness of books under the head but the back was still hollowed, you could come and lift and move the hips in such a way that the back flattened. Now, we all thought this was a splendid idea but when we demonstrated it to FM he was quite horrified and said, "No, that's all wrong! Instead of encouraging natural release to take place, you're actually doing something!" And the same is true if you're lying down without the aid of a teacher. All you can do is direct to lengthen and widen thereby freeing the torso. If you do that, then gravity should take the arch down and if it doesn't do that, then that's just bad luck.

In general, FM used to advise us that the best way to proceed in a lesson is to start someone in the chair and see how they're going and then put them on the table and see if you can get a bit more lengthening, freedom and release. Once that's been achieved the teacher can take the pupil up and work once more with the chair to see if the improvement that's been got on the table can be sustained. If it can't, FM's advice was to put the pupil back on the table once more.

FM also showed us a few ways of getting people off the table. One way was to take one of the pupil's legs down and then take them straight up into sitting before taking the legs around. A variation on this is to take both legs down – but not fully extended – before sitting the pupil up. The way I take people off the table now developed out of the problem I faced working with a woman with severe rheumatoid arthritis who was working in the office at Ashley Place. The thing was to be able to swing her round and get her sitting up as quickly as possible before she'd even had time to think and stiffen up.

In taking pupils off the table, in general, you want to forestall either their wish to help or, more usually, the fear reaction which causes stiffening and contraction. However, if I find someone who is very nervous and frightened, I don't even attempt to take them up, I just ask them to get up themselves.

Lying down is not mentioned in any of Alexander's books, is it?

No, that's quite right. But then FM wasn't writing "how-to" books. But he certainly encouraged his pupils and the students on the training course to lie down.

Was it something Alexander himself practised?

Not as far as I know.

But it's something you do?

Absolutely. If you've been pulling down, it helps you to straighten out, get into better shape and improve the basic co-ordination. Nowadays, I tend to lie on my teaching table but when I used to lie on the floor, I liked going into a squat – I'd let the knees go forward and away, put out my hands and gently lower myself onto the floor.

How did "monkey" start?

That must have come about through FM's work with various voice teachers and, I've no doubt, through gymnasium or physical training of some sort – perhaps Swedish drill. In fact, there's an interesting line that I've never been able to follow up and that concerns a Frenchman called François Delsarte, who lived in Paris in the early nineteenth century. He made a study of gesture – what nowadays we call "body language" – and created a system for teaching actors. I remember that FM used to illustrate that a pickpocket or sneak-thief who wanted to draw the attention of one of his accomplices would beckon like this by wriggling the little finger. So FM had certainly studied the Delsarte system, and in the early days it was one of the things that he taught. It's also clear from what I've been able to find out that Delsarte had some rudimentary ideas about the use of the body. This would have naturally interested FM, who was fascinated by anything to do with use. Indeed, when he was young the first modern bicycles – you know, ones with equal-sized wheels – were imported into Australia. He was very proud of the fact that he'd observed others riding these machines, had worked out what was involved, and then had mounted one for the first time and had ridden it successfully for three miles without falling off.

Another thing he was involved in was the roller-skating craze of the time. I remember his sister, Amy, telling me that one of FM's party pieces was skating backwards and jumping obstacles. He also made a study of fencing and later decided to play the violin, although he wasn't particularly keen on music. Moreover he had a longstanding interest in riding and horses, and his brother, AR, was a much sought-after amateur jockey. I don't know though if FM was ever involved in race riding. But all this boils down to the fact that he'd obviously given a lot of time and thought to the observation of how people use themselves doing all sorts of things. And "monkey" is, of course, part of the whole range of movement activities, from skiing to roller skating and horse riding.

The important thing to remember about "monkey" is that it involves bending the knees in order to lower the centre of gravity. It creates stability. FM called it a "position of mechanical advantage"; it was the students who called it "monkey". In fact, I'm not sure that he called it anything to begin with – I think it was some of his doctor friends who called it a "position of mechanical advantage". He had had four or five doctors amongst his group of original pupils in Auckland, and when discussing and demonstrating things he got feedback from people with a medical training. I'm sure that's how he acquired a lot of his knowledge about anatomy and physiology.

Now, monkey is meant to be a position of mechanical advantage, as you rightly observe, but I think a lot of people experience it as a position of mechanical disadvantage. Furthermore, I recall you once telling me that monkey is one of those attitudes where you really can trust your feelings: in short, if it's painful or uncomfortable or, rather, if it's more painful and uncomfortable than being upright – something's wrong or amiss. So what's the basic mistake that people make in performing it?

When they move into monkey they stiffen and put pressure on the joints instead of releasing to move and taking pressure off the joints. It all works on the principle of counterbalance – if you get that correct, then everything is light and free. It's the same problem people have when they go to sit in the chair. Instead of letting the knees go to sit, they bend the knees and stiffen. The other problem with monkey is that people are apt to look upon it as a fixed position which makes for rigidity.

So he was doing "monkey": at what point then did he decide to put his hands on the back rail of a chair?

That came from FM's observations of people doing exercises in an attempt to increase their chest capacity. Whether he'd seen these exercises performed by gymnastic or so-called breathing and voice teachers, I'm not sure. But there was an exercise in which people were instructed to get hold of the back of a chair and pull. They thought it expanded the chest, and this exercise was popular when chest expansion was all the rage. So FM studied it and tried it out, but came to the conclusion that it was having the opposite effect to the one intended: it was particularly noticeable that when someone pulled on the back of the chair they produced a lot of tension which tended to contract the chest rather than expand it. He then set out to find a way of doing it that would promote expansion. Of course, it's also a procedure that involved the use of the hands, and FM was very interested in that.

So in the Alexander version, which way are you meant to pull?

33

If you've got all the directions working correctly – if you're length-ening and achieving the pull to the elbows and widening of the upper part of the arms, the resulting pull is not something you really have to think about. It's the outcome – the result, if you like – of all the other forces involved.

There is no pull as such, then?

Not really. For example, if I put my fingertips on the table which is in front of me and I'm directing my elbow away from my fin-gertips, it obviously can't move very much, but it moves as far as it can. When you pull like that with ulnar deviation – the wrists curved slightly inwards towards one another – and the chair is fixed, then, as FM used to point out, if you pull too strongly you won't be able to keep the ulnar deviation. The wrist will straighten in other words. That's the measure you're overdoing it.

Alexander was very insistent that the fingers and thumb should be straight and flat against the rail of the chair, wasn't he?

Yes, because people are habitually accustomed to using a flexor grip. What Alexander wanted was to give people an experience of using the extensors and thus to employ an extensor grip. If you flex the fingers from the first knuckle that's an extensor rather than a flexor grip.

Are there better or worse chairs for this procedure?

Ideally there are, I suppose. But FM never bothered about that too much. All you want is a straight-back chair with a fairly high back – a conventional dining-room chair is adequate to the task.

And the experience gained in putting hands over the back of the chair is applicable to everyday life – it's not some arcane ritual, is it?

Absolutely not. If you're manipulating objects – picking up a ket-tle or taking hold of a car steering wheel – you want as much extension as possible. And, if you're going to pick something up – you might be using quite a lot of force – you'll find that it's a very big advantage to get as much extension as you can to form the basis for going into flexion. The temptation that has to be resisted is to go into flexion straight away, when you'll end up with very much less power. It's a principle very well understood by good weight-lifters, for instance.

And, in my experience, good golfers, too.

Yes, all the pundits say you need to get a very, very firm grip so that the club doesn't shift in your hand at the moment of impact. But what a lot of golfers don't realise or appreciate is that you need the extension first and then, when you come to fold your hands onto the club, you get a very firm grip. What they nearly all tend to concentrate on is the grip on its own but that only makes them tighten and pull down. Another good example is the use of the arms in firing a twelve-bore shotgun. Now, what you've got to do with the weapon before you bring it to the shoulders is to throw it away before bringing it back. This stops you snatching it and tightening everything up. Similarly, FM used to say that when the average violinist picks up the violin and bow, they're finished before they've begun because they've tightened and pulled down. In fact, some violin teachers realise this and tell their pupils to take the violin by the neck and swing it away from the body before bringing it to the shoulder. That's going along the right lines. And they've obviously come to that conclusion through experience and observation.

And the whispered "ah"?

Once again it's something he must have worked out very early on. With all his experiments he knew a lot about the workings of the vocal mechanisms, and no doubt it was through experimentation that he concluded that the whispered "ah" was a very effective procedure. In fact, it's one of the nearest things to an exercise in the Alexander Technique. Nearly everyone's breathing habits are defective and most vocal training systems focus on breathing in – actually taking a breath before the start of something – with little or no understanding of how to get a controlled exhalation.

FM's point was, therefore, a simple one: it is useless to learn how to breathe in if you don't know how to breathe out.

Did he claim that the whispered "ah" had beneficial effects?

He did indeed. He used to say: "You ask me what a whispered 'ah' is good for and I ask you to tell me what it isn't good for!" He also said that if he wasn't such an idiot, he'd do a lot more whispered "ahs" himself. He valued the whispered "ah" very highly.

Why was Alexander so insistent that the procedure begin with thinking of something funny to smile about?

Probably, the most important thing of all is the psychological effect, which leads to more freedom and less contraction. Of course, there are technical advantages as well. For example, it takes the upper lip off the teeth, affects the back of the throat and soft palate and frees the facial muscles, which makes it easier for the mouth to open. But when you're performing whispered "ahs" you're not paying attention to the effects of the smile as such; you're just focusing on something amusing and you keep it going. The smile sets the scene, in other words.

Do you think it's useful to slide the lower jaw forward so that the lower teeth oppose the upper teeth, before allowing the jaw to open?

If you look at the anatomy of the jaw joint, the mouth will only open properly when the jaw slides forward. But, it should slide forward because of the release facilitated by the smile. It's also one of the reasons why FM instructed that the tip of the tongue be placed to the top of the lower teeth. It's the difference between releasing the jaw and getting it to go forward by indirect means and trying to do it directly. FM would certainly not have been in favour of doing it directly.

So the tongue touching the lower teeth should be its normal resting place?

Yes, very definitely. It was one of the things FM used to recommend for people who had an unsatisfactory occlusion, especially if the jaw was habitually pulled in and the bite was underslung.

Do you direct the ribs in any way?

Well, you've got to remember that the whole set-up is biased in favour of expansion. People are apt to forget that the diaphragm is a muscle of inhalation and not a muscle of exhalation. So it's only the contraction that requires conscious attention. The ribs are naturally disposed to contract after exhalation but, often, they do need encouragement.

And what ribs are we are talking about here?

The floating ribs. And bear in mind they're almost totally at the back of the torso – they hardly come round the front at all.

Is it true that, to help breathing, Alexander used to encourage those of his pupils with narrow nasal passages to massage the nose?

Yes, just at the base of the nostrils – a sensitive spot where the muscles of the *alae nasi* are situated. He used to encourage people to do it with a drop of warm olive oil.

How did creeping on all fours develop?

That's something that developed after FM's death. It came through Professor Raymond Dart's influence. Dart had some lessons from Irene Tasker in South Africa in the 1940s and as a result wrote three papers: the first for physiotherapists, "The Double-Spiral Arrangement of the Voluntary Musculature"; the second for doctors, "The Attainment of Poise"; and finally for dentists, "The Postural Aspects of Malocclusion". These are now available as part of a book.* Incidentally, although "The Double Spiral" paper was written first, it didn't get published until after the other two had come out. FM read the three papers and was very impressed. I

---

* Raymond A. Dart *Skill and Poise* (1996).

think I'm right in saying that he only met Dart on one occasion, although they did correspond from time to time. I remember being very excited when I read the papers, although I didn't have a sufficient knowledge of physiology and anatomy really to appreciate them. I gave Dart a lesson the time he met FM – this was in London in 1949 – and after that we kept in touch.

In the sixties Dart was taken up by Glenn Doman and Carl Delacato at the Institutes For the Achievement of Human Potential in Philadelphia and Dart saw an interesting connection between the work being done at the Institutes with brain-damaged children and the Alexander Technique. He thought it would be a good idea if we got together. So he invited Dilys and me to Philadelphia in 1966 to do the "orientation course". This had been set up for heads of schools, colleges and institutions in order to familiarise them with the work of the Institutes – its procedures, programmes, and so on. At the Institutes we learned a great deal about the development of infant behaviour, which convinced us to take a closer look at creeping – one of the things Dart was keen on. In my opinion, it's a very useful procedure – and not just for those who have been classified as brain-damaged. In fact, I think we are all brain-damaged to some degree, and creeping allows one to pinpoint defects in growth and development as well as defects in neuromuscular co-ordination. The people at the Institutes rightly point out that creeping is an essential stage in infant development – all babies go through it with a greater or lesser degree of success.

Common sense indicates that people who did not learn to creep at the appropriate time can still benefit enormously by learning it properly as adults, and thus improve their co-ordination. I might add that it's also a tremendously powerful tool in opening up the hands and the shoulders.

In performing creeping, it's very important to get a satisfactory initial attitude: you want the arms and thighs pretty well vertical so that the weight is distributed reliably and evenly on the hands and knees. It's also critical not to drop the neck downwards. It has to be remembered that the neck is part of the spine and a continuation of the back. So with the head leading the way, the spine lengthens and the whole organism tends towards mobility.

What sort of attitude should the hands take?

Well, you're using your hands as feet and it's worthwhile bringing the fingers together so you get an arch in the hands. Once you've got the initial set-up, you can practise rocking forwards and backwards, freeing the ankles and wrists, whilst maintaining length and not stiffening in any way before going into creeping proper using different patterns and rhythms.

How, in your view, is the creeping you teach different to how a baby performs it?

Well, we're aiming to get adults to produce a movement similar to a well co-ordinated baby. It has to be remembered that not all babies creep very efficiently or very well.

But one obvious difference is that a baby will swing or pull the arm through, taking the hand off the floor, whereas the way you teach it involves keeping the hand and, indeed, the knee and the foot in contact with the floor, doesn't it?

Yes, that comes from the Doman-Delacato procedures. By sliding the hand, leg and foot through along the ground you get more sensory stimulus that way.

You obviously see it as a very important procedure.

Yes, I do.

Do you think that the different traditions in the Alexander Technique reflect the personalities of the founders? Or have the different traditions emerged out of the varied opportunities for teaching the Technique: Marjorie Barstow, for example, taught in groups because, as she admits, it was a group situation that first provided her with a chance to teach?*

---

* Marjorie Barstow's preface to F. M. Alexander *The Use Of The Self* (1984).

Yes, I think it's fairly obvious that the personalities of the people concerned have made a significant impact on the way the Technique has been taught. For example, Pat Macdonald was very interested in boxing, Wilfred Barlow in medicine, and I was fascinated by the character and personality of Alexander himself. Then, of course, the way in which the various schools emerged often reflected the situations of the time. I'd say that's true for Britain and for other countries like the USA. Indeed, if we take North America as an example, Judith Liebowitz, the founder of the American Center for the Alexander Technique (ACAT), who had worked for a long time with Lulie Westfeldt and Alma Frank, saw an opportunity to teach in the 1950s and started a training course in New York with Debbie Caplan (who, by the way, is Alma Frank's daughter). Neither Judith nor Debbie had been formally trained, as it were, but both had learned a great deal over the years: Judith Liebowitz was a remarkable woman for whom I had a very high regard. She had very severe handicaps after she contracted polio as a youngster and she coped with them marvellously. She was very courageous and obviously put a great deal of thought – and successfully so – into freeing and lengthening herself. She had remarkable use and I'm sure that was why she was so popular and sought-after, especially by dancers. Anyway, Judy and Debbie set up a two-year training course and although it suffered from a number of inadequacies and shortcomings, some of the people who went through the training have gone on to become established and competent teachers – Frank Ottiwell who lives in San Francisco is a good example.

In Britain, the Barlows started a training course while FM was still alive. They knew this move would incur FM's displeasure, but as they'd already quarrelled with him some years earlier, I doubt they were concerned. Later, we – that is to say, some of the assistant teachers at Ashley Place – had some legal problems with Beaumont Alexander, FM's youngest brother, who was a co-trustee of FM's estate. As a result of this we walked out and he brought in Pat Macdonald, who had been teaching independently in Cardiff, and appointed him Principal of the new "Alexander Foundation" that he had set up.

Pat then started a training course and trained a number of Israelis who finished their training course in about 1960, and subsequently, after they had completed seven years teaching, opened up another training course in Jerusalem. Previously, Charles Neal and Eric de Peyer had started another training course here at 18 Lansdowne Road, but that was discontinued after Charles's death in 1958. At a later time Pat Macdonald announced his intention to go to America; some of his students who weren't willing to follow him transferred to another training course authorised by the Society of Teachers of the Alexander Technique (STAT) and headed by Peter Scott, who had been working with Pat for a number of years. Either Macdonald never went to the States, or went and came back, but in any case he continued teaching in London so that the overall situation in the late 1960s was that there were four training courses in London – Scott's, Macdonald's, the Barlows', and our own – with one in New York and one in Israel. Since then quite a few more have emerged, of course.

So from what you've just said it would seem that a lot of these developments were *ad hoc* responses to prevailing conditions, with little or no control or even much overall direction.

That's right. It was all *ad hoc*! People found that they'd been teaching for a number of years and that pupils were coming to them asking if they could train as Alexander teachers, so it seemed a good idea to set up a training course. They then applied to STAT for permission, and if that was granted they went about their business. Of course, there have been problems, but overall these developments show that people really do appreciate the importance and value of the work.

How do you evaluate the differences of approach of the various Alexander schools and traditions?

It's difficult to be categorical about these things, but for the most part I think that the differences are much more apparent than

41

real. An unprejudiced person taking an objective view would, I think, draw the conclusion that the differences are not fundamental.

You wouldn't subscribe to the view that under the umbrella term "The Alexander Technique" there are several quite distinct practices going on?

No, I wouldn't really. We all accuse each other of not teaching to principle – not teaching correctly – but I think the various schools have different emphases rather than do totally different things.

My impression is that Dr Barlow viewed the Technique from a medical perspective, but, on the other hand, a great deal of the work in his establishment was carried out by his wife, who doesn't really see the Technique in those terms at all. In fact, I think that as FM's niece she feels she has a keen responsibility to see that her uncle's work isn't distorted or misrepresented, and she's always tried to keep the teaching as orthodox as possible – and rightly so. Pat Macdonald always approached the Technique from a practical point of view. He wasn't by nature a philosopher and always wanted to teach in a simple, direct way. My one reservation is that his teachers tend to rather over-simplify and thus teach in a somewhat stereotyped way. Indeed, as far as I know Pat Macdonald didn't really enter into questions as to how the Technique should be applied to everyday life. If, for example, someone went to Pat and told him that they were a violinist and were having trouble with their bowing arm, he would give them his standard work and then say, "Well, now you know what the Technique is all about, so it's up to you to sort out your bowing arm." However, some of his students reported that he gave them excellent help.

How would you approach a similar sort of situation?

It depends on the person, of course, but like Marjorie Barstow I'd probably say: "Look, bring in your violin and let me have a look at what you do." Then I'd try and explain to the pupil what they're doing and what the consequences are.

You told me once that you didn't think that there were many teachers who approached the Technique exclusively from a body mechanics point of view and that anyway to do so is a cop-out. Could you elaborate?

Well, we are, after all, primarily concerned with inhibition – this is the key to the Technique – and inhibition depends on conscious control, which obviously takes us beyond the realm of body mechanics. Another point to bear in mind is that everybody has deep, unconscious emotional and psychological problems, although people are often reluctant to acknowledge these things. If an Alexander teacher dealt simply in body mechanics it might be possible to get away from all that, but at the same time to do so wouldn't be very valuable. In fact, such teaching would be extremely naive.

That's very interesting. It leads me to ask whether Alexander dealt directly with people's emotional and psychological problems in the context of the training course?

The answer is: no, he definitely did not. He didn't deal with them at all. I rather think he walked away from it. It was something he didn't want to recognise or know anything about.

Because he was an unemotional man?

Well, I wouldn't say he was unemotional, but I think that he found himself out of his depth trying to tackle this kind of issue in a group situation. He could certainly deal with the emotional problems of individuals, but not those of a group. Indeed, my own experience of this whole area leads me to believe that indirect means work best: I've found that if you can keep students from getting bored and instead keep them interested and reasonably cheerful, they'll tend not to get too intense about these issues. It's the general atmosphere that one needs to keep an eye on: that's the way we've always worked anyway. It's inevitable that during training people do go through a tremendous number of emotional crises. Now I think it's important for them to realise that, while people are concerned for them – they are considered and valued as individuals – and are willing to give them support, a great deal of the trauma must just be worked through individually. A major problem inevitably arises when people come to the Technique. They find that it's possible, with the aid of a teacher, to be lighter and freer and thus to reach a level they can't reach by themselves. That means, of course, that they'll lose it and fall back. It also means that they become aware that there's a considerable gap between their best and their worst. And when they're down they feel even more fed-up and depressed than usual because they've known what it's like to be up there. And there's not an awful lot that they can do about it.

This feeling of depression is understandable, but for many people their feelings easily connect to their previous educational experiences, say, at school or college – you know, the "I'm not very good at anything" bit – and so they tend to play on these past failures. And, as I say, there's not a lot one can do about it except to make sympathetic noises and try to help them as much as possible to work through it.

Your attitude on these matters seems to be this: it's inevitable that people will go through whatever they have to go through and the best way to deal with it is to adopt a non-judgemental attitude as far as possible. Is that a fair summary?

Yes, that's absolutely right. I think to do otherwise confuses the issue. On the other hand, I recognise that there are people who suffer from serious pathological states and they very definitely need help. But, in my opinion, they need the best professional help available. They certainly don't need things like co-counselling and amateur psychology any more than they need amateur brain surgery. In these cases psychiatrists and psychotherapists have an important contribution to make.

I know you don't endorse the practice of some training courses in allowing students to work on members of the public. Could you say why?

Some teachers think it's a good idea for students to have bodies to practise on, and invite members of the public along for that purpose. The public are willing to go along with this because they feel that they're getting cheap work – possibly work they couldn't otherwise afford – and you can see their point of view. However, I have two objections to this: the first is that I think it's a good idea to postpone the day when students are faced with a real teaching situation for as long as possible. This goes back to the discussion we had earlier, when I pointed out that in the deliberately artificial situation on the training course where students are working on their fellow students, they are carefully building up habits that will keep them on the right lines when they are in a real teaching situation. To repeat: there's no advantage in students dealing with the real teaching situation until they absolutely have to. Another relevant issue here is that fellow students are much more critical and therefore more difficult to work on than any member of the general public.

My second objection does not come from the perspective of the students on training courses, but from that of the general public. When ordinary people are going to have Alexander lessons, they must have proper lessons. They need a teacher who is going to give some thought to their problems. It's terribly unfair to have someone drop in to a training course and be worked on by inexperienced students: the visitor will get a very poor experience of the Technique. Yet I do agree with the point made some years ago by Wilfred Barlow at a STAT meeting that newly qualified teachers ought to take every possible opportunity to use their hands, even if that means giving talks and demonstrations without pay. In any case, it's much better than sitting around at home waiting for people to book a lesson. But this should be done after qualifying and not before.

Are there any other points of disagreement worth clarifying?

Well, the Macdonald way of teaching with the feet very far apart is not something I would do. In any case it's something Pat developed himself and it definitely didn't originate from anything FM

45

did. Of course, FM used to point out – and the assistant teachers found – that when a new pupil comes and stands in front of the chair they will tend to have their feet close together.

The first thing a teacher asks a pupil is to put their feet slightly further apart, because you want them to have the free use and movement of the legs as they sit and stand: if the feet are too close together the legs tend to stiffen. So that's something that's always been part of the Alexander Technique.

However, I'm not sure how Macdonald came to the feet-far-apart approach. The first encounter I had with it was in the 1960s, when he was working as Principal at the Alexander Foundation. I'd previously broken my leg and when Pat was giving me a turn he got me to put my feet wide apart. At the time, I didn't think anything of it: I just thought that he was doing that to help me with my particular problem. I was, therefore, surprised to find out later on that he was doing it with everyone. Of course we were then curious to find out what lay behind the procedure. Indeed, there was a celebrated occasion at a STAT meeting at Sonia Lushington's place just off Sloane Square when someone asked Pat why he was teaching in that way. His reply was that it was easier for his students, but added that once they'd learned the procedure, they didn't have to carry on teaching in that particular way. But as we all know it does become habitual and they do continue to teach in that way.

I've got a nice little demonstration that I give from time to time where I show exactly what Pat Macdonald meant when he says it's easier to get people in and out of the chair with their feet wide apart. You can have the most pulled down and generally unco-operative individual imaginable, but if you set it up so that they have their feet a good distance away from one another, it's almost impossible for them to prevent you moving them in and out of the chair – simply because so much is done with the leg muscles. This approach is perfectly reasonable if a teacher's objective is to find an easy way of getting people in and out of the chair. But if the teacher's aim is to change the pupil's thought processes and he is therefore working not on the "physical" aspect of the procedure but on the giving and withholding of consent, to make it so easy to move in and out of the chair doesn't give the pupil any understanding of either inhibition or direction.

Another procedure I would disagree with is the one outlined in Dr Barlow's book* where the reader is encouraged to experiment with flattening the back whilst leaning against a wall. Once again, Alexander didn't teach this, in my experience, and it's very different from lying down in a semi-supine position where the objective is to get people to free up the spine, resulting in a flattening of the back. That's fine because the spine isn't weight-bearing when they're lying down like that. When someone is standing, however, then the spine certainly is weight-bearing and the curves are needed – not exaggerated or distorted curves of course – not least because they allow the primary control to function efficiently.

While we're on the subject of disagreements, I'm sure that people in other schools object to what we do in creeping. They'd probably say, for example, that creeping encourages people to pull their heads back to see where they're going. That's not true, of course, but one can appreciate that misunderstandings can occur.

But one disagreement that is fundamental is the attitude towards the positions of mechanical advantage or "monkey". I can't give an overview of the attitude of heads of other schools on this subject, but I attach tremendous importance to this procedure. On our training course, we spend a lot of time and trouble ensuring that people learn to do it properly. In contrast, however, Frank Pierce Jones, who was something of an authority on the Technique even if he never ran a training course (although there are people in America who would claim that they were trained by him), wouldn't teach monkey because he considered that people stiffened and did it so badly that it wasn't useful. My argument is that people can indeed do it badly, but when they learn to do it properly it transforms the whole use of their hands as well as their whole approach to teaching. I cannot exaggerate its importance,

---

* Wilfred Barlow *The Alexander Principle* (1975), pp. 146–47.

and there's no doubt that Alexander saw it as crucial. Of course, when I quote FM on these matters, I'm perfectly aware that he wasn't the pope and that just because he said something doesn't mean that he was right: I'm prepared to allow the possibility that he was completely wrong. Indeed, it seems to me that in all these issues we've been discussing, it's a matter of experiment and trying things out to find out for oneself. For instance, if someone shows me something useful, I'm all in favour of adopting it. That's how we got on to saddle work, for example.

How did that start?

Just before FM died in 1955, he started giving lessons to a little girl of four-and-a-half with spina bifida. She hadn't the use of her legs, so she couldn't stand and it was also difficult for her to sit. FM's contention was that if he could get her to stand there was a possibility that he could get her to walk. Unfortunately she had had only about three weeks' work when he died, and it was left to us, therefore, to continue. We didn't have anything like FM's skill and expertise in these matters and wondered what would be the best approach to the problem. Then, one day someone suggested that it might be a good idea to use a toy donkey: the little girl would find it fun to sit on and it would be easier for us to work on her. We went out and got a toy donkey and it worked out very well, because we could get her sitting on her sitting bones relatively easily and then work on her legs.

Time went on and she grew and became too big for the donkey, so we substituted a four-legged trestle with a padded seat. Then someone – I've forgotten who – very sensibly suggested that we use a proper saddle. This was a distinct improvement because it was more secure and certainly more comfortable. After this initial experiment we started to put other people on the saddle and found it tremendously helpful in working on people's legs. That motivated us to get a special saddle-horse made rather than continue with the bits and pieces we'd been improvising with. Undoubtedly, a teacher can do a lot more with the saddle than either with the chair or the table, not least because gravity is a tremendous help in lengthening the legs. In fact, I've found that a number of people who experience pain in the lumbar and sacro-iliac areas when standing and lying down can become free of pain – albeit temporarily – when seated on the saddle. However, I do not use it all the time or as a matter of course, but it's certainly something we teach the students on the training course.

Presumably, saddle-work is a very useful preliminary procedure for someone who is interested in learning how to ride?

Oh, yes! When you're in the saddle the weight is very positively taken on the seat bones and the legs are less involved than, say, when someone's sitting on a chair. It means the normal interference from the legs and around the hip-joints is largely eliminated. In this way, the balance of the body is maintained from the seat-bones by the musculature of the trunk. And it's very useful for someone to get a sense of that so that when they do get on a horse they're not so nervous and not so inclined to grip up.

You also became interested in John Gorman's work and research as outlined in his book, *The Cause of Lumbar Back Pain and the Solution**, didn't you?

Yes, we first came across his ideas after someone spotted an advertisement in *Horse and Hound* about a book giving a remedy for back pain. They wrote in asking for details and when John Gorman replied it turned out that he was a mechanical engineer who'd used his knowledge to try and find a cure for his own persistent and chronic back pain. Apparently he'd been to everyone and had all the usual treatments, none of which had helped him. He then, like FM, decided that because no one could tell him what was wrong with his back he'd try and find out for himself. Eventually, he came to the conclusion that a lot of his problems stemmed from the way he was sitting and so he experimented with different ways of sitting until his back pain abated. That led him into

---

* John Gorman *The Cause of Lumbar Back Pain and the Solution* (1983).

the whole area of seat and chair design, but not really to the over-all problem of use, which was FM's particular interest.

Anyway we got in touch – he lives in Basingstoke – and he came up to London to talk to us about his ideas on the spine. As far as I understand him, he maintains that the vast majority of western people are restricted in their ability to use the hip joints. This means they can't squat properly and therefore don't have a full range of movement. He argues that when people sit in a conventional chair and bring their thighs to something like a right angle with their spine, there is a great deal of constriction in the hip joint which, in turn, causes the pelvis to move and pulls on the spine particularly in the lumbar area. Eventually this leads to displacement of the lumbar vertebrae, which manifests itself as sciatica and other problems.

It was a fascinating talk and, although he didn't know anything about the Alexander Technique, I gave him a demonstration and a few things to read. He was extremely interested because, as he rightly said, he approaches the problem of lumbar back pain from a mechanical point of view, whereas we approach it from the practical perspective of movement, use and habit. Nonetheless, we ended up with a very valuable and complementary perspective on the problems of the lower back. Returning to our earlier discussion about saddle work, it's obvious that when someone sits on the saddle their legs are not at right angles to the spine and so there's every possibility of freeing the hip joint and increasing the range of movement of the legs at the same time as the individual is sitting on the seat bones in a balanced way. This means there's an opportunity to rectify the distortions in the lumbar area.

Of course, a lot of office and home workers use the backless "Balans" chair where the seat is forward tilting and the legs are bent under supported by a knee rest. What do you make of those?

Well, the trouble with those is that they feel fine when you just sit in them, but after you've been there for a while you might as well be kneeling for all intents and purposes. And that only puts a lot of pressure on the knee joints and, to some extent, on the hip joints. It encourages people to go down on the joints instead of coming up off them. But, at the end of the day, not even a good chair is an effective substitute for getting an improved use. As Alexander rightly observed: "We want to improve the people, not the furniture."

You mentioned that many westerners can't squat very easily, but when Alexander demonstrates this procedure in the short film of him shot in 1949 and 1950 it's a very impressive sequence.* The thing that stands out is that he's got remarkably springy, elastic legs, and particularly so when it's considered that he was around 80 years of age at the time.

The thing is, if you have it from childhood, you don't want to lose it. And I don't think FM ever lost it. What he shows in the film is that he's got the balance right. If you look at a lot of young children, they have it too.

So why do you think most people do lose it?

I think potty-training is the thing that puts most children wrong. Instead of keeping the antagonistic pulls and counterbalance involved in a proper squat they've got the pot to sit on and that interferes with the postural mechanisms.

You're not saying that potty-training should be eliminated, are you?

No, I don't think it's necessary to go that far. So long as children are encouraged to perform squatting when they're playing and so on they'll maintain the skill.

Do you think that that springy, elastic quality that Alexander demonstrates in the film is realistically attainable by most adults, particularly once it's been lost?

---

* *F. M. Alexander – narrated by Walter H. M. Carrington* (1992).

Yes, it's what you're aiming for. If people really want it, then they can probably get it with perseverance.

So would you say that some squatting is better than no squatting at all, especially for people with a sedentary lifestyle?

I think it probably is. Certainly FM thought so – he used to encourage us to squat. When I was training we didn't have tables but instead worked with people on the floor: we had to squat. FM considered it one of those things people ought to be able to do. But he never made a big issue out of it – that wasn't his way. He considered that the most important elements of the Technique were inhibition and direction, and that if you gave people specific things to do like squatting or even putting their hands on the backs of chairs – here I'm talking about private pupils – they would go away and "do" them at the expense of the thought and care needed to master inhibition and direction.

They'd be better off lying down?

Yes, they'd be better off lying down. Or, at any rate, just moving around doing ordinary everyday things with a bit of thought. And, of course, FM would have listed squatting as one of those everyday things.

There'd be no point in going away and doing a daily regime of, say, one hundred squats?

No, not at all. That's exercise. That was totally foreign to FM's outlook.

Do you think that long periods of sitting at school resulting in boredom and tiredness is an additional element in explaining why many children lose their springy connectedness? Indeed, didn't George Coghill say some very negative things about the chair?

Yes, he said the chair was "the most atrocious invention hygienically that man ever perpetrated." And, undoubtedly, continuous sitting does a lot of harm. But I think a lot of modern educationalists have come around to that view and children are allowed to move around a lot more than they used to in primary schools. They don't endlessly sit in rows of desks like we did. And it's true for anyone really – child or adult – that it's good idea to get up and move around. If I'm dealing with writers or journalists I tell them that it's very bad to sit for more than about half an hour.

Are there any other factors that account for the deterioration in use amongst many children? Further, how can they be avoided?

Our experience with children at the "little school" at Penhill and elsewhere indicates that the biggest factors making for change are, shall we say, emotional or psychological. It's normally around the age of three years of age that many children leave the protection of the home environment – they've been playing with their siblings or whatever – and they start to encounter strangers for the first time. It's then that they need all sorts of measures to boost their confidence and image of self-worth and deal with any attacks or criticism that might be directed their way. And, of course, other children can be very cruel, particularly if a child has a visible defect or problem. So it's not just the "physical" aspect of things that needs to be taken account of, but also rather the child's need to feel supported and regarded in the round, as it were. And what's very important is for the child to learn inhibition, because if they can learn to control their responses and reactions by saying "No" it gives them more freedom to select and do what they really want to do.

Professor Raymond Dart utilised any number of static and dynamic attitudes and movements – indeed, we discussed creeping on all fours earlier – in the pursuit of bodily poise and equilibrium. How do you assess what are now known as the Dart procedures?

I think some background is relevant here: when Dart's Alexander teacher, Irene Tasker, left South Africa to come back to England, he and other pupils were left without a teacher. Because they valued the work, they got together from time to time to consider how they could help each other and themselves. All of them, including Dart, derived great benefit from lying in semi-supine with their heads supported by a pile of books. Dart then decided to pursue his investigations by lying prone and performing various other activities. The point I wish to make – and here I'm drawing on my conversations with Dart – is that he spent a good deal of time following and examining these procedures – he was setting aside at least half-an-hour a day for all this – and naturally he brought his anatomical knowledge to bear. He also used various perspectives derived from his work in physical anthropology. These two disciplines provided him with invaluable information, not only on the development of the individual (ontogeny), but also of the species (phylogeny) in moving from one stage of development to another. I know, for instance, that he was particularly keen on the example of use and movement offered by the crocodile: this great big animal lies with its belly in the mud and then uses its limbs to lift itself up before moving off.

Dart used the idea that, roughly speaking, ontogeny recapitulates phylogeny, and tried to find out how the body could support itself in prone before moving in such a way that the body is supported by the limbs. In his papers, he states that one of the main things that leads to muscle tension and spasm is fear or anxiety: indeed, he considered that the basic fear is that of falling. Then he reasoned that, by lying in prone in a relatively good way, there was an opportunity to overcome the fear of falling and thus learn how to move in a different way and with maximum security.

Dart also stated in his papers that if anyone follows the procedures he recommends, they too can learn a tremendous amount, but, I would say in parentheses, particularly if they happen to be professors of anatomy with an extensive knowledge of physical anthropology! I'm sceptical about what an individual without specialised knowledge would get from performing the Dart procedures. One obvious reason for this is that people would only be relying on their subjective sensations to know if they were doing it correctly or not – how much tension they were making, how much shortening and contraction was involved and so on. The Alexander Technique as we teach it is intended to introduce people to non-doing rather than doing. Now, the Dart procedures are quite an interesting form of doing but I don't think they've got tremendous relevance to the Technique, except if you're looking around for things to apply it to. In that sense, the Dart procedures are comparable to, say, Tai Chi or whatever. I never teach the Dart procedures on the training course; I don't consider that they're worthwhile unless somebody's curious and wants to know about them. And, from the perspective of an Alexander teacher, I must also say that I know people are only too fond of doing exercises and I certainly wouldn't want to encourage them to develop in that way. In my opinion, people need to be discouraged from doing specific exercises.

Why is that?

All they're doing is making the muscular system more rigid. All our experience indicates that what people need to learn is how to use the muscles totally differently. The ordinary concept of exercise in which you're putting a demand on the muscles and using them strongly is totally misconceived. Instead, you want to economise on muscular effort as far as possible. You don't want to use any more muscular strength than is necessary for the task in hand. Exercises that involve the strong use of muscle for their own sake are completely futile, counterproductive and really quite dangerous. Activities like muscle-building are really based on a misconception of the mechanics of the organism. It has to be remembered that the fundamental human requirement is to achieve balance on two feet or in whatever attitude is being employed at the time. But balance can only be achieved dynamically – if there's any rigidity or fixation it endangers and imperils balance. It's only when the structure is free and mobile that the balance can be achieved safely. FM was always saying that all muscular effort tends to make for thoracic rigidity and he was quite correct – the one thing you don't want is thoracic rigidity. So the less muscular effort you make for a particular activity the better. Of course, that doesn't mean to say that when necessary you can't use all available strength. There are situations and occasions where you need to use strength. However, if you're going to do that, then it has to be foreseen and carefully prepared for and rehearsed beforehand. For the average person living in an urban environment, the less muscular effort they use in their daily routine the better.

Yes, it's interesting that it's urban folk who are most inclined to go to the gym and utilise various exercise machines. The average farmer or coal-miner is not hurrying to the sports centre at the end of the day to engage in a strenuous workout, are they?

Absolutely not. A farmer or miner who lives a life of constant muscular effort doesn't need to go to the gym. Until the advent of mechanisation, farming and mining were dependent on muscular effort and, if people were going to do it successfully over many years, they had to find the best way of doing it. They certainly didn't need to perform any further or different exercise than that involved in their work. And, of course, until very recent times nearly everyone – even people living in cities – walked a great deal more than they do today. Now, walking is a very good form of exercise and one that should involve maximum mobility and economy of effort.

But what advice would you give to people who do wish to pursue more aerobically demanding pursuits like running, swimming or cycling?

Well, the conditions required in these activities have been worked out through experience and are known to good coaches. And there's always a positive element of doing – you're going to run up a hill, swim thirty lengths or whatever. Now, the Technique says that's all fine – go ahead and do it, but make absolutely sure that, in the process of doing it, you don't stiffen the neck, pull the head back or in any other way shorten in stature. But people are inclined to get things out of context: they say things like, "I'd like to get myself better and more efficient. I'd like to be healthier and fitter." Well, Alexander would have said: "Fitness for what?" As soon as you introduce the notion of "for what?" you've got the idea of a task – demands have to be met, in other words – and you've then got to work out how to meet those demands, which is what FM meant by the term "means whereby". Now, a lot of people who go running, swimming, cycling or whatever think they're getting fit, without giving any thought to the technique or style in which they're doing things. In all these activities, as I said before, there are certain demands to be met. And Alexander says that you will meet them most efficiently if you observe the proper working of the primary control. But let me make it clear; if you go out running and just say: "Neck to be free, head to go forward and up, back to lengthen and widen" it won't do any good at all. It may be enjoyable, but that's another matter. Repeating the words is of no value in itself. If you're going to run, you've got to run in such a way that you keep your length, don't pull your head back and, of course, don't interfere with the breathing. In other words, you use yourself properly to run.

We've talked quite a lot about training courses in this section, so it seems relevant to ask you what you think are the guiding principles for a successful training school?

A lot of it depends on seeing what's going on on a day-to-day and week-by-week basis. As you work, you get fresh insights, and as long as you're able to devise slightly different approaches, the work keeps alive and moving forward. I'd say that the main principle is a negative one: take as much care as possible and try not to fall into routine and habit, where everything becomes staid and static. Each day should be approached on an experimental basis. Once you start stereotyping the work, you're in serious trouble. That's why I've always been ready to make a change in the programme and lay on something different from the ordinary routine. But having said that, it's also useful to bear in mind that certain ways of proceeding – such as working in small groups and getting people to work on each other in a deliberately artificial way rather than for real as on some training courses – seem to be consistently effective practices.

I might add that one problem in running a training course – in running anything, really – is to get people to arrive on time. I always take the view that I'm supposed to be dealing with responsible adults and, if anyone is late or doesn't turn up, I assume there's a good reason for it. Obviously this isn't always the case, but I think it's best to work on this assumption.

You don't wield a big stick?

No, I don't wield a big stick. That's a very dangerous thing to do. The Technique is all about people learning to take responsibility for themselves. Wielding a big stick or whatever inevitably invites people to give somebody else the responsibility. A director of a training course shouldn't impose anything on the individual. In fact, people should be encouraged to find and develop their individuality. Learning the Technique involves certain requirements of inhibition and direction, but it's up to the individual to work out an application relevant to their own situation and circumstances.

Recently, some people have questioned the traditional and intensive three-year training procedure for teachers and have advocated a more flexible, open-ended approach, perhaps even including courses at weekends. How do you assess things?

I'm very much in favour of the traditional method of training teachers. The trainee has to recognise that they are learning to be the tool used in conveying the relevant experience to the pupil. The use of the hands requires a tremendous amount of application and it can only be learnt by constant monitoring and practice. Having said that, I think the Technique can be learned on part-time courses, say, where people train in the morning and then work the rest of the day, but even that's not very satisfactory. But weekend training has two associated problems: first, it has to be recognised that people have strongly established habits and, if students don't have the necessary frequency of work, they go back all too easily to those established habits. Secondly, if people are doing full-time jobs – particularly, if they're demanding jobs –

they're really too tired to train. People have to realise that training isn't an intellectual matter but one of actually getting the sensory experience – the feel, if you like – aided by people of sufficient experience who can watch and help. The number of hours required in training is, to some extent, an arbitrary matter, but you do have to have a measure and 1600 hours over three years is the one we've come up with.

The other problem with part-time courses is that it very easily leads to part-time teaching, which I'm very much against. People should be encouraged to take as much opportunity to teach the Technique as they can possibly manage. If people are teaching the Technique part-time, one suspects they're only applying the Technique to themselves part-time. And the simple fact is that the Technique doesn't work on a part-time basis. As my mother used to say: "You've got to live it." If people are going to teach it, they need to be working at it full-time, or at least working towards it. It's only by working at it that you get the chance to learn what it's all about.

Part II

Context

Dr Barlow has written: "I found in Alexander an imaginative genius I have not seen outmatched by anyone. I think he transformed the human condition, although as yet on a tiny scale."* Would you agree with this assessment – was FM really a genius?

I suppose it depends on how you define the word genius; I don't know the definition of genius. FM certainly was a unique personality and quite unlike anyone else I've ever come across. Moreover, there's no doubt about the significance of his work and the importance of his discovery – not least because, as modern research goes on and new advances are made, the claims of FM are frequently confirmed and endorsed. So, if one wants to call famous innovators geniuses, then, yes, FM must have been a genius.

But from a slightly different angle, it's a reasonable conjecture that, if FM hadn't discovered the Technique, it's by no means certain that anyone else would have – in fact, no one else has as far as I know – so that now, without FM, we wouldn't have a system comparable to the Alexander Technique.

Yes, I think that's absolutely right. One has to remember that when FM discovered the Technique, Rudolph Magnus, who was professor of pharmacology at the University of Utrecht, hadn't even begun his pioneering research into the physiology of posture. I don't know exactly when Magnus started his work, but the

---

* Wilfred Barlow *The Alexander Principle* (1975), p. 199.

results weren't published until 1924. And we're talking about Alexander actually beginning to teach in 1894, with the fundamental observations made in the previous decade or so. Furthermore, Magnus' work never suggested to anyone anything like a technique or a way of making practical use of his discoveries relating to the importance of the head-neck reflexes in posture and movement. As far as I'm aware, all the work in that field has been built upon the premise – implicit and explicit – that how people use themselves is the outcome of habit and a variety of subconscious processes. The idea of taking conscious control of use in Alexander's sense isn't something that anyone really considered. In fact, although by the 1920s and '30s there were various people saying that the primary function of the nervous system was an inhibitory one, the concept that the central function of the brain – of consciousness, if you like – is not to initiate movement but to control it is something that has only recently emerged. In 1986 I managed to get hold of a copy of an article by Benjamin Libet, a neurologist working at the University of California, San Francisco, in which he tries to substantiate the claim that behavioural responses are initiated or generated in the subconscious or, as he would say, the unconscious, and only rise into consciousness for a fraction of a second before they become operative in terms of activity.

He claims that at the point before activity there is some sort of window on the process when the individual may suddenly realise what is likely to happen and, at that moment, there is a possibility that they can either give or withhold consent. That means, in effect, that one can either carry on and do it, or else abort the operation. But, claims Libet, one can't modify the course of action once it's been initiated: one is already then committed to the way it is to be done. The basic argument is neatly summarised in the following passage:

> I propose the thesis that conscious volitional control may operate
> not to initiate the volitional process but to select and control it,
> either by permitting or triggering the final motor outcome of the

unconsciously initiated process or by vetoing the progression to actual motor activation.*

Now, Libet is very highly regarded in his field – indeed, he worked in Australia for some time with Sir John Eccles – so this is a fascinating example of a relatively recent development in the field, but it's something that FM had seen and, crucially, developed into a technique by 1894! It's easy, then, to make a case that Alexander was years ahead of his time.

You've met Libet, haven't you?

Yes, we met him in 1989 when Chris Stevens invited him to the training course he was running at the time in Denmark. Later on, he came here to the Constructive Teaching Centre and gave a lecture to a group of Alexander teachers. He's a very nice man. He had Alexander lessons all the time he was in contact with us and enjoyed them very much.

Now, you connected Libet's perspective to your experience of the Alexander Technique, but did Libet make a similar connection through his lessons to his academic research?

I couldn't say that. What I can say is that he was a good pupil and certainly he didn't disagree with anything we were doing.

Do you think that Alexander's youthfulness – he would have been in his late teens and early twenties when he was working out his discovery – was a critical factor in his success?

Yes, very definitely and positively. He was a young man seeking to achieve and realise his ambition. An older person, for example, might well have been less enthusiastic about pursuing matters. And we have to bear in mind that he came from an environment – the outback – where life was a constant contest and struggle with nature, and people were obliged to be resourceful in order to survive.

* Benjamin Libet "Unconscious cerebral initiative and the role of conscious will in voluntary action" (1985).

It seems to me that he was also lucky that his initial hunch that his vocal problems were caused by something that he was doing to himself turned out to be true. After all, they could have been caused by some mysterious organic factor or, perhaps worse, a combination of misuse and a mysterious organic factor. All his observations and calculations, concerning what was causing what, might well have come to naught in either case.

Yes, he was lucky. And he considered himself to be lucky. Furthermore, he thought there was something "lucky", so to speak, in the Technique. He certainly considered there was something about it that would keep it going and save it from destruction.

I remember you once said that Alexander wasn't a very patient man but that he was very persistent. Could you say some more about that?

He had tremendous energy, good observation and a very quick brain. He didn't suffer fools gladly and had to exercise restraint when he found himself dealing with people who lag behind. Although he could be patient, it was an effort for him. He found it difficult to come to terms with the fact that the average man or woman is slow on the uptake. Yet, having said that, it's fair to point out that FM wasn't a particularly vain man – he was too much of a realist – and thought of himself as an average person with moderate capabilities. He considered that anything he could do and understand, anyone else could too, quite easily. And as for people like George Bernard Shaw and Aldous Huxley, he assumed they would grasp things in a flash! He thought that the idea of having to explain things to them was preposterous and an insult to their intelligence!

Do you think, then, that he underestimated his abilities?

Yes, I think he underestimated his capacities tremendously – calamitously, really – and this underestimation prevented a lot of worthwhile communication with a number of people who came into contact with the Technique. For example, although Shaw and FM enjoyed each other's company and had a great deal of mutual respect and affection, there was never anything like a meeting of minds. Similarly, FM had a lot of sympathy and feeling for Aldous Huxley, not least because he appreciated Aldous' difficulties and handicaps. He also thought that Aldous had an absolutely first-rate brain and was a great publicist of the Technique, and yet I'm pretty sure they never got down to the nuts and bolts of the Technique. And I'm also sure that one of the things that affected FM's relationship with Huxley was that he didn't have the patience or inclination to interest himself in the mystical stuff that Aldous and his friend, Gerald Heard, were interested in. In fact, FM regarded a lot of Aldous' enthusiasms as a complete waste of time. The idea of carrying out experiments with mescaline and so on would have been completely abhorrent to FM.

Why is that?

First and foremost because Alexander was all for the development of consciousness and the employment of the conscious, reasoning faculty rather than the cultivation of the subconscious. He wanted the conscious mind to be "quickened" – and, of course, "quickened" is the old-fashioned word for brought alive – but anything like mescaline is artificial in its effect. He was quite explicit about this. It's worth quoting him here:

> It is essential that the peoples of civilisation should comprehend the value of their inheritance, that outcome of the long process of evolution which will enable them to govern the uses of their own physical mechanisms. . . . This triumph is not to be won in sleep, in trance, in submission, in paralysis, or in anaesthesia, but in a clear, open-eyed, reasoning, deliberate consciousness and apprehension of the wonderful potentialities possessed by mankind, the transcendent inheritance of a conscious mind.*

---

* F. M. Alexander *Man's Supreme Inheritance* (1996), p. 146.

But one of the few "thinkers" that he managed to communicate with reasonably well was Professor John Dewey of Columbia University, although even here I doubt there was a real meeting of minds. Dewey was an original thinker, but his background was in some ways comparable to Alexander's. Both men were born into rural communities – Dewey in New England and Alexander in Tasmania.

They both knew what living off the land entailed, and they also valued education and the arts. In fact, the two found it rather difficult to adjust to people who were knowledgeable in academic matters but who couldn't plough a field or wield an axe; they just took such skills for granted and that must have influenced their outlooks. I also think it's fair to say that Dewey drew on Alexander and Alexander drew on Dewey. Indeed, *Constructive Conscious Control of the Individual* is really a monument to their relationship because, I've been told, they sat down together and went through the manuscript word by word and sentence by sentence, arguing it every inch of the way. So it was Alexander's book, but it also owed a tremendous amount to Dewey.

Dewey derived enormous benefit from his lessons, not least because it increased his suppleness and co-ordination. Further, it had never occurred to him that the process of thinking could actually be applied to the "physical" use of himself. That was quite a revelation because until then thinking had meant a type of reflection thinking which, in his case, resulted in serious and adverse consequences on his breathing. Put simply, Dewey would go into a state of deep thought and not breathe very much at all. And that's very dangerous, particularly if it's kept up continually. It's why Alexander told Dewey that he shouldn't work for more than half an hour at a stretch; instead he should get up, move around and do something to break things up a bit.

Because of his experiences with the Technique, Dewey felt strongly that Alexander's work needed to be investigated and established – he was quite confident that it could be established –

---

* Frank Pierce Jones *Freedom to Change* (1997).

and that's one of the main reasons why he gave such encouragement to Frank Pierce Jones's investigations.

Some of Frank Pierce Jones's scientific research (as well his personal recollection of the time he spent with FM and AR Alexander) are available in his book, *Freedom to Change*. How do you assess this work?

I don't think it's the definitive book on the Technique or anything like that, but it's a very valuable contribution. Frank Pierce Jones, as I said, was Dewey's protégé, and Dewey was anxious to get someone to do the necessary scientific work relating the Technique to anatomy, physiology and so on. Considering that Frank was a classical scholar and not a scientist, he did a remarkably good job. Of course, Frank died prematurely before the book came out, and even before it was in final form. All sorts of things might have been different had he lived longer. In any case, his knowledge of anatomy and physiology, though no doubt derived from sound sources, was not of a level to satisfy professional scientists working in those fields. I don't think there is anything wrong with what he said, but the danger of that sort of work is that it falls between two stools: it's too technical for the layperson, who anyway doesn't have the equipment to evaluate whether it's right or not, and too amateurish for the serious scientist, who won't take the time and trouble to investigate it further. The exception was Raymond Dart. But Dart was so immersed in the fields of anatomy and physical anthropology when he encountered the Technique that it didn't matter to him what Frank Pierce Jones may or may not have said. Through his experience of the Technique, Dart was able to make the necessary anatomical and physiological connections right away. It's my guess that, if Dewey had said to Dart that it would be a good idea if someone investigated the anatomical and physiological implications of the Technique, Dart would have said it would be a complete waste of time.

Everything on that side of things that needed to be done had already been done; what people needed to do was to go ahead and learn it. Dart was always completely dismissive of anybody's attempts to investigate what people call the "scientific basis of the Technique" because, as he says, to anyone who knows anything, the "scientific" basis of the Technique is self-evident. In any case, to seek legitimation from scientific authority is rather pointless: when it comes down to it no one is really a useful authority. If the Almighty Himself came down from heaven people would find some objection. Yet, having said that, certain things investigated by Frank are very useful indeed – his work on the startle pattern, for example. That's tremendously good and useful from a practical teaching point of view.

This is what Jones calls the stereotypical response to a loud noise: it involves changes in head poise and a wave-like contraction through the body, taking in the shoulders, arms, chest and, in severe cases, the legs. Put simply, it's shortening in stature, as Alexander would have termed it, albeit in dramatic form.

Yes, Frank goes on to point out that the startle pattern is the paradigm for the sort of changes you find in sickness, old age or lack of exercise. It really does indicate along general lines how people do pull down and mess themselves up in one way or another. Now if you can show people the startle pattern and get them to understand the mechanics of it, it indicates both what we're aiming for and what we're trying to avoid. The startle pattern is very much associated with anxiety and fear – it's a response, shall we say, that is negative rather than positive in its effects. For example, take someone who suffers from stage-fright – perhaps they've got to give a presentation or an after-dinner speech – if they realise the sort of pattern they're liable to get into, it helps them to understand the positive reasons for freeing the neck, directing the head forward and up, and so on.

This isn't really the place to get into a detailed account of Jones's work, but he raises a number of interesting issues, three of which I'd like to hear you comment on. First, Jones questions whether reported improvements in health can be used as a means of defining or measuring the efficiency of the Alexander Technique.

Now, it's a well known problem for medical researchers that people can experience an increase in subjective well-being – they "feel better", in other words – but objectively they can be deteriorating. It's one of the reasons why the placebo response is constantly monitored and taken into account in medical trials of one sort or another. So I can understand where Jones is coming from. And yet Alexander was concerned with objective improvements in health, was he not?

Well, the Technique originated because FM found that his discovery of the working of the primary control did lead to improvements in his voice and breathing. And if you look at *Man's Supreme Inheritance* and, in particular, his remarks on respiratory re-education, Alexander talks about changes in skin colour and an overall improvement in general functioning in his pupils. For Alexander breathing was the main focus and consideration of his work. People have sometimes queried how it was that Alexander knew he was right and what criteria he used to assess and analyse matters, but the criteria were perfectly obvious and straightforward: first, he wasn't sucking and grasping for air; and second, the quality of his voice was getting stronger.

In evaluating the Technique the other criterion Jones questions is whether "posture", especially the use of before and after photographs, is of any value. His reasoning is interesting: he doesn't deny that still photographs will often reveal interesting changes of one sort or another, it's just that practitioners of other disciplines can produce exactly the same sort of evidence. He goes on: "I once showed some of those still photographs to a doctor at Harvard and he assured me that in the Physical Education Department they made these changes all the time."* He prefers the change in movement pattern, which, he claims, tends to be smoother, more regular and mechanically efficient as the defining characteristic of the Alexander Technique. Do you agree with his proposals?

---

* Frank Pierce Jones *Freedom to Change* (1997) p. 190.

Well, on the subject of before and after photographs, it's interesting that FM thought exactly the same as Frank. FM thought you couldn't put them forward as evidence – not reliably, anyway – as they are either too easily faked or simple evidence of apparent but not necessarily real changes. On the other hand, I've certainly seen some photographs before and after a course of lessons and people have looked quite strikingly different – you know, someone who was very round-shouldered and narrow-chested has really opened out. In these sorts of cases it was to me evident that the change visible in the photographs was the outcome of the lessons because I was there to witness it. As for the movement pattern, all I can say is that Frank found it useful from his point of view. I don't think the ordinary Alexander teacher would necessarily find it useful. I think that what really differentiates the Alexander Technique from lots of other things is the emphasis on inhibition – on learning to prevent the wrong, rather than trying to do the right, thing. In most other disciplines and teachings, the emphasis is very much on getting or doing something right.

Finally, Jones observes that FM lost interest in nearly all of his pupils once he'd made the major changes.* Do you think that was all part and parcel of the impatient aspect of his character?

That's hard to say. I think any teacher realises that when a pupil comes to them for lessons there are changes to be made and things to teach them. It's not so much that you lose interest, but that you have done what you set out to do. What happens after that is primarily up to the pupil. When most of us have learned the rudiments of the Technique and have some experience of putting it into practice, we long for more help, and we'd prefer somebody to do it for us rather than do it ourselves. I think a point comes when an individual has to assume responsibility for him or herself and drop the pilot.

Before the pilot drops them?

---

* Frank Pierce Jones *Freedom to Change* (1997) p. 68.

Yes. Part of the pilot's responsibility is to say: "Well, now you're on your own, chum!"

Was Alexander a genuinely cheerful man or was he just acting a part?

Yes, he was cheerful. There was nothing pompous or artificial about him. He had a spontaneous good humour. He always said that as a young man he had a quick and violent temper, and in later life I think there were still times when he had to control his temper – he did get angry and upset occasionally, like all of us, really. But certainly there was a lot of laughter on the training course. And he was always very good with children – setting them at their ease and keeping them amused. And, of course, he believed that for people to benefit and to apply the Technique they needed, so to speak, to think of something funny to smile.

He wanted people to cultivate a cheerful disposition, then?

Certainly. Nowadays his sense of humour might not be considered tremendously sophisticated by some people. He was amused by childish jokes, and he was turned off by vulgar or salacious humour. When in the company of people telling coarse jokes, FM's laughter was rather forced – there was an undercurrent of disapproval. But he could tell what Victorians would have called risqué stories, although those tales were far from our contemporary humour. He was an example of Victorian constraints.

A bit of a puritan, then?

Yes. But that was his cultural background, after all.

Was he a very expressive man?

He was quiet, really. In ordinary things, he never moved his upper arms away from his sides unless he was engaged in something that required it. But he used his voice expressively. Very definitely. The other thing about him was his keen observation and the quickness and liveliness of his eyes, which took in everything that was going on around him and, in particular, what was of relevance to the person he was working on. You didn't see FM drift off into non-seeing or day-dreaming, for example. He was very, very observant.

Did he move quickly or slowly, say, in walking?

Oh, fairly quickly. All his movements were fairly quick.

He was, of course, a migrant. People who leave one society and settle in another are apt to see things differently from the natives.

I suppose they do.

But did Alexander come across as an expatriate Australian or did he take on and cultivate the trappings and outlook of conventional, bourgeois society?

What you've got to remember is that he was an actor and one of the rôles he was definitely playing was of member of the establishment. He knew that his work was so unorthodox and revolutionary that he saw it as important that the persona he adopted should be as conventional and orthodox as possible so as not to . . .

Frighten the horses?

Exactly.

Did he ever give you any hint of the irony of the situation?

Not really. He used to say that you had to conform to convention and so on. And he would advise you to do so. For instance, he disapproved of people who didn't dress tidily, smartly and correctly. But you've got to remember that we now live in a different age altogether. There were so many conventions that people observed without question in those days, but they've all disappeared now.

Did he show any interest in political matters?

He did, but it's not easy to give a straightforward answer to this question. He'd had a lot of experience – or, at least, his uncle had

– with bad labour relations in Australia. So he was rather anti-trade union and opposed to the idea of organised labour. In fact, he was opposed to the idea of organised anything. He wasn't a collectivist, but there again, on the other hand, he was very anti-"stuffed shirt" – and although I can't exactly remember, I think he had some sympathy for Neville Chamberlain. But he was very anti-Churchill.

He used to say: "Churchill is incapable of understanding anything that his grandfather hadn't understood." It's always been thought that FM's attitude to Churchill stemmed from the fact that Churchill's wife, Clementine, had come to FM as a pupil but said that on no account must her husband know that she was having lessons.

But FM was friendly with Sir Stafford Cripps. Again, I'm not sure to what extent there was a meeting of minds, but FM considered Cripps an able man and admired his humanitarian sympathy in trying to eradicate poverty. FM pitied the poor and the socially deprived, and didn't like the class structure. Yet, at the same time, he strongly believed in self-help and felt that even if people sought outside help they should try to help themselves. Still, it's interesting and perhaps revealing that a number of pupils were on the Labour side: Charles Trevelyan was the first Labour Minister of Education and there was also Eleanor Rathbone, one of the first Labour women MPs, of course. FM had a strong feeling for the ideals of these people, but pointed out that people needed to address themselves practically to the correction of the wrong, rather than to the pursuit of grandiose idealistic schemes for social change.

He obviously wasn't a utopian, then?

No, he wasn't.

We talked in the first section about the Technique as involving a philosophy of life that might be compared to a religious attitude, so an obvious question is: what was FM's philosophy of life?

Well, I've just said that FM wasn't utopian. In fact, he was, rather, an advocate of moderation in all things. He believed in enjoying what he regarded as the good things in life, but not in excess, and he thought that people should give proper thought and consideration to see that they weren't over-indulging. Although FM smoked – he loved a fine cigar – drank the best that was available and loved good food, he was always on the abstemious side.

You also mentioned that he wasn't a conventionally religious man.

Far from it. He had little use for organised religion, although he had some good friends among the clergy. He did, however, come from a religious family – I think they were Calvinists – but his faith ended after his mother gave birth to a son, John, who had a tumour on the brain and screamed from the moment he was born until he died three months later. The baby was obviously in constant pain, and there was nothing anyone could do about it.

It must have been a searing experience for everyone involved; it certainly affected FM. He used to say that for any parson or religious person to talk about a caring, personal god was nonsense when he'd witnessed such incredible suffering at first hand. The experience led FM to close his mind completely to the possibility that the religious teachers could be right.

Would you describe him as an agnostic?

To choose a word to sum up his attitude is difficult, but I suppose agnostic might do. He used to say that he believed in nothing and he believed in everything. In many ways he had a strong religious attitude, because he not only valued and respected life but also had what we nowadays call a holistic outlook. He believed with Hamlet that there is a destiny that shapes our end. Perhaps the best summary of his attitude is encapsulated in Schweitzer's phrase "reverence for life", although personally I've never liked that phrase, because I've always asked: "What about reverence for death?" Why such a partial view? On a universal scale there are obviously things that are as important as life.

I take it that Alexander didn't speculate on the possibility of an afterlife.

I think he felt that it was something you weren't going to know about until the time came. You see, he wasn't an intellectual man. Or, perhaps I should say that he wasn't a man with what we would call intellectual interests. The things that someone like Shaw or Huxley might have enjoyed talking about wouldn't really have interested FM.

Yet it's quite interesting, given that absence of intellectual interests, that he wrote four books.

Well the books are very practical and, as FM himself said, there isn't anything in them that wasn't the outcome of his experience, whereas other people produce books from imagination, speculation, etc. FM's books are concrete and practical, because he wasn't interested in speculation. His negative attitude to religion extended also to philosophy, economics, sociology and the major speculative intellectual fields.

Was Alexander's aphorism that belief is a matter of customary muscle tension simply designed to shock people, or was there a more serious element behind it?

He was perfectly serious about it, because he equated belief with fixation. In his experience a rigidity of mind corresponded to a rigidity of body. His approach to belief was different from that of the majority of people. It's perhaps too easy to call non-believers sceptics but, as I understand it, FM's attitude to life in general was comparable to his attitude towards horse racing. As far as he was concerned nothing was better than a racing certainty. If you're a racing man and take a great deal of trouble to work out the form and weigh everything up, you're absolutely certain that you're on to a good thing. You think that this horse has to be it. Now you can call that belief or what you will, but it's certainly a positive determination of mind. But then having made that decision, a quarter of an hour or so later, the horse has lost and come nowhere. You don't get upset about it, nor do you try to prove to yourself that it really must have won in spite of what everyone has said. No: you just accept the fact that it wasn't so and pass on to deal with something else. You don't cling to your beliefs; you're willing to discard them in the light of experience. That must be a valuable capability and, of course, a lot of people don't have it.

So do you think Alexander's attitude to life came from his racing experiences or did his racing experiences simply express that kind of assumption about life anyway?

I don't know really. It's an interesting question; but, in any case, I'm sure that it went pretty deep. Perhaps I should add here that, as far as I could see, the other important element in FM's character was that he was steeped in Shakespeare and found that plays like *Hamlet* and *The Merchant of Venice* provided a vivid expression of his own attitude to life. He was always quoting Shakespeare, and one of his favourite quotations was: "To thine own self be true". I suppose you could say he believed that, but the use of the term belief here isn't the same as someone reciting a religious creed. He considered that the latter was associated with muscle tension and that "believers" of all sorts were apt to be particularly ripe examples of neuromuscular hypertension.

In *Man's Supreme Inheritance**, Alexander counsels parents not to contaminate babies' milk with sugar which, he warns darkly, would lead to all sorts of internal troubles. Further, he advises that children need to cultivate a taste for "wholesome, nourishing food".

Yes, I recall that.

It raises the question as to whether Alexander was more or less directly concerned with his pupils' dietary habits?

Well, he didn't offer advice unless it was asked for. And it has to be remembered that he was on very close terms with Dr

---

* F. M. Alexander *Man's Supreme Inheritance* (1996), p. 69.

McDonagh, who had very strong views about diets. McDonagh believed that people consistently poisoned themselves by what they ate and drank. It was why he would treat people by taking a blood sample and then preparing a vaccine based on it. He also got people to have a course of colonic irrigation which, undoubtedly, washed away a lot of the intestinal flora. After this, he would administer the vaccine to re-establish healthier gut flora. McDonagh believed that all disease was one and that health depended on the state of the protein particles in the blood plasma. He instructed people to watch their diet and gave everyone a standard diet sheet. It wasn't a vegetarian regime – it allowed for a certain amount of meat and fish – but it was, nevertheless, a fairly restricted diet, especially in terms of quantity. But both McDonagh and FM advocated that people should eat fruit and vegetables of the very best quality.

Another interesting aspect of McDonagh's regime concerned the problem of habit. He was very much concerned whether people were eating the same sort of food at the same time, day in and day out. He thus advised people to rotate foodstuffs. In that way, even if you had a passion for a certain food, if you obeyed the rotation rule you weren't likely to over-indulge and eat too much of it.

Dietary rotation would find favour with current experts, but is there any evidence that McDonagh's vaccine did any good?

I don't know really. In any case, I don't think McDonagh was the only doctor who did this. He certainly had impeccable qualifications, had a Harley Street practice and was very well regarded.

Did all of Alexander's pupils go to McDonagh?

No, not by any means. But if somebody came along and we thought they needed some medical advice we'd send them to see McDonagh or some other relevant specialist.

Did your mother visit McDonagh?

No, she didn't. She had in any case worked out for herself through experience and medical advice the relevant dietary information. But it was through her lessons with Alexander that the breakthrough came. By taking her up and getting the primary control going, it relieved the pressure she was creating in herself. And I think her experience shows that dietary manipulation without modification of the primary control is often doomed to failure, as FM often pointed out.

During Alexander's lifetime there were a number of important developments – studies in psychoanalysis, body therapies emerging out of Wilhelm Reich's work, and so on. First, was FM aware of these developments, and second, did he express any opinion about them?

Yes, he was aware of a lot of these things. It's fair to say that he was strongly prejudiced against Freud, although I suspect that his knowledge of the Freudian and post-Freudian literature was limited. Nevertheless, his attitude towards psychoanalysis, for example, was determined by the consideration that Freud compartmentalised or separated mind and body: Alexander considered that to be fundamentally wrong. Because psychoanalysis started from the wrong premise, he didn't think there was much in the psychoanalytic corpus worth pursuing.

He was also sceptical of other things around at the time – the Bates method, for example. He considered that, although there was a lot of good sense in some of the things that Bates argued, it was no good simply working on the eyes unless one also worked on the organism as a whole. Moreover, FM maintained that, if one worked on the organism as a whole, then by the time a reasonable job had been done, it wouldn't be necessary to work specifically on the eyes. This attitude led to a disagreement with Aldous Huxley about the Bates Method, and FM certainly didn't much care for Aldous's *The Art of Seeing*.

Aldous and his friend, Gerald Heard, were always discovering new self-improvement techniques, but to Alexander they were all based on the wrong principle. They proceeded on the assumption that you could rationally determine what was right and then, having established this, you could set about putting it into operation. FM always contended that it's almost impossible to know what's right, but that one could with time patiently establish what is wrong and then set up measures to avoid it. That seemed to him, and indeed it seems to me, an absolutely fundamental difference.

What did Alexander think of osteopathy?

He was very much against it, although Dr McDonagh was rather in favour of it. McDonagh thought that Alexander was right in his approach to the problem of use, but from a practical standpoint he knew it just wasn't possible for all the people he saw in his surgery to have Alexander lessons because, at that time, there were very few Alexander teachers. In his view, osteopathy was better than nothing.

Presumably FM's objections were similar to those he held about the Bates Method: osteopathy was specific and piecemeal.

Yes. And, very importantly, Alexander didn't believe in the manipulative approach. He was very much opposed to the underlying theory in osteopathy regarding lesions and their correction through manipulation, because it entirely disregarded the influence of use on functioning. I don't think that the Alexander Technique and osteopathy mix at all. I would qualify that by allowing that cranial osteopathy, with the emphasis on the relationship between the sacrum and cranium – the two ends of the spine – seems to be proceeding along lines unlike those of conventional osteopathy.

But what causes trouble is when people are having Alexander lessons and then have repeated osteopathic manipulations. As far as I can discover, the results are: first, the inherent nature of the procedure involves what osteopaths call "soft tissue" work – some means like massage is used to soften up the area – before it's possible to perform manipulation. If this is done a number of times one finds that the ligaments and tissue are quite literally loosened up, so that the stability of, say, a joint is lost and it doesn't take very much to put it out again. That is very dangerous. Second, in our work, although I know a lot of people get confused by it, we are trying to establish a more reliable sensory appreciation – one that is as reliable as possible, in fact. In contrast to this, osteopathic manipulation actually seems to disrupt sensory appreciation and has a disorienting effect. This means that if someone has had a number of Alexander lessons and has a feeling that warns them when they're pulling down and pulling the head back, having osteopathic manipulation upsets the sensory register and they don't know how to proceed.

I've actually experienced this myself. Through the McDonagh situation I wanted to have some osteopathy, in order to have first-hand experience of it and to see what it was actually like. I discussed the issue with Alexander and, although he was willing for me to do it, I don't think he was wildly enthusiastic about it. But I was glad I did it while he was alive, because I did experience this sense of disorientation and was very relieved to get back to his hands and get the proper co-ordination re-established. So that was my subjective experience at the time, and it's also been confirmed by other people who've had lessons with me since then.

Do you think osteopathy or, indeed, spinal manipulation in general have much relevance to people who experience pain and discomfort after some one-off movement – perhaps, they've picked up a very heavy suitcase or done too much gardening – that is outside their normal movement range?

I think that's a complex question. In very simple terms, I'd say that manipulation is not very useful and rest is much to be preferred. On the other hand, it depends on the quality and skill of the osteopath: a cranial osteopath, for example, might well take a similar view to one I've expressed that rest is the best policy. However, the patient might well be experiencing a lot of anxiety and if they do go for a treatment they at least feel something's been done – although I think what actually is done often comes under the heading of "witchcraft and black magic"! Put it this way, if you or

I did something strange and injured ourselves then it would be better to rest and get somebody to take the head to ensure that there wasn't too much pulling down going on. Of course, with certain conditions like frozen shoulder or tennis elbow, sacro-cranial osteopathy can be very helpful. These conditions do require treatment and fall outside the scope of the Alexander Technique.

You don't consider that, by improving the general co-ordination, these specific problems will be helped or alleviated in any way?

Yes, in time. But it's like when people are suffering from asthma or bronchitis: obviously they need their general use improved, but it's going to take time and they need specific treatments as well.

And this would be your attitude if a pupil developed something in the course of having lessons?

Oh, yes. I've often recommended people to a couple of cranial osteopaths whose work I know is both highly skilful and beneficial.

Given your appraisal of conventional osteopathy, what is your assessment of deep-tissue therapy and massage?

Massage is a terribly bad thing, except for the most superficial kind of massage. Massage that amounts to little more than skin friction is harmless and probably beneficial, but deep massage is something else again.

Like osteopathy it can damage tissue, ligaments and so on?

It can do, yes. So can Rolfing – at least, Rolfing as it was originally practised.

Now, practitioners of Rolfing and its offshoots like Hellerwork claim that it's only by getting deep access to the musculature – in particular, the fascia – that real and effective change is possible. From that point of view, the Alexander Technique must appear a very light and surface sort of endeavour, don't you think?

Ida Rolf certainly claimed that the fascia had to be changed. However, Alexander used to say that this might be perfectly true from a physiological point of view, but questioned whether this was the place to make the change. He maintained that it was far better to leave these things alone and make the best use of what you have got available. If you do go and interfere at other levels and undo something, it might create more problems than it solves.

Are you saying that it's better to approach matters indirectly?

Yes, certainly. When an Alexander teacher puts their hands on, they're not trying to get a change as defined by Rolfing, Hellerwork or whatever but to improve the pupil's sensory guidance, which is necessary to obtain direction. For example, take the rib-cage movement: if you're going to manipulate and actually move the ribs because they're fixed and so on, you'll run into all sorts of problems and difficulties. However, by contrast, if you're encouraging people to think and direct in such a way that they're bringing about the type of change and conditions that will eventually allow the ribs to free, then it's a different matter altogether. And that's not just a theoretical point – it's something FM had learned from experience.

You mean he'd tried the other way and found it wanting?

Yes. All that's likely to happen is that the intercostal muscles will be strained. And, of course, where the ribs articulate to the spine, the joints are very small and delicate, so any form of direct manipulation can result in damage. FM preferred to encourage people to let go of the ribs so that they could contract. As I pointed out earlier, under normal conditions of functioning the tendency of the ribs is to open out and expand. What, therefore, needs to be watched is the contraction as the lengthening and widening take place in a co-ordinated and balanced way, thus facilitating free rib movement.

In general terms, FM always used to say that the real issue was the direction in which the tide was flowing. If things are flowing in the right direction that's fine: be prepared to wait as long as it takes. It would be very foolish to try and hustle things along. If, on the other hand, the tide is running the other way, then you must try everything you possibly can to stop and prevent it flowing in that direction. Alexander was very positive about this. He wasn't looking for a big change – he was satisfied with a very small amount of change in inhibition and direction.

I realise that people will never reach a consensus in their attitudes to particular individuals but it's interesting, nonetheless, that FM aroused such strong and diverse opinions. Lulie Westfeldt (*op cit.*), for example, whilst admiring and deriving obvious benefit from the Technique, clearly didn't particularly like Alexander, whereas others like Peggy Williams found him to be extremely compassionate. How do you account for these differences?

I don't think Lulie was fair to FM. She had had very severe polio, which resulted in her having very fixed ankles and it meant she walked awkwardly. FM helped her transform her whole way of moving so that even with her fixed ankles she was able to minimise the consequences. The first time I met her was when she had come over from America to visit the training course in 1937 or 1938. Now, you could see she suffered from polio but, in general, she moved very well. But her account is strongly coloured by an experience that wasn't FM's fault nor, for that matter, hers. What happened was this: after she finished training, Lulie went back to teach in New York. As far as I know she was reasonably happy and making progress. She used to come back to London in the summer months to work with the teachers and students who had been on the training course with her. At that stage she might well have thought that FM didn't do as much as he might to put pupils her way or show much positive appreciation of her capabilities as a teacher, but I don't think she had any great chip on her shoulder. In fact, FM was teaching in New York in 1942 and 1943, and I imagine Lulie had some lessons from him. Their relationship must have been all right because she came over to England again in 1945 or 1946.

But around 1948 or 1949 a letter from a professional man in New York arrived at Ashley Place, asking for the recommendation of a teacher in his area. Without FM's knowledge, the enquirer received an answer from John Skinner saying that there was no one in the New York area that Mr Alexander would recommend. That meant the cat was really amongst the pigeons. The prospective pupil told Lulie Westfeldt what had happened and she felt that the rug had been pulled from under her feet – she was absolutely shattered – because she felt she'd made considerable progress and had served the work well. In fact, she wrote to me – I think I've still got the letter somewhere – telling about the whole episode and saying she was almost certainly going to cancel her proposed trip to England in a few months' time. She said that, even if she made the journey, nothing would induce her to cross the threshold of Ashley Place and have anything to do with that wicked old man! She added she would like to work with me, but not at Ashley Place.

I wrote back that I didn't think FM had been directly involved and, in any case, she had to bear in mind that he was an old man – this all happened after his eightieth birthday – and he obviously wasn't going to be around much longer; refusing to see him and work with him was not rational and was like cutting off her nose to spite her face. However, she didn't take my advice and that was the end of that! I had no more contact with her until after the book was published, when she returned to England and we met again. We had a nice time and I prevailed on her to visit the training course and do some work with the students. Again, that went well, and she left saying that she was definitely going to come back the following year and work with us, but then she died almost as soon as she stepped off the boat in New York.

Had she modified her opinions of Alexander?

Not about FM very much, but she'd modified them about me and the value of the work! She'd definitely softened a great deal. But she wrote that book at a moment when she was feeling extremely bitter and let down. So I think one has to allow for that.

The book undoubtedly gives a prejudiced account of FM, but I suppose in the circumstances understandably so.

But you're right that other people found FM to be a caring and compassionate man. I think that when people with problems and difficulties came to have lessons with him, they felt that here was somebody who was on their side and concerned for them, who would be interested to help if he possibly could. But people find fault with anybody, don't they? These judgements are so subjective that it's difficult to arrive at a "final" conclusion.

And yet, it seems to me, that in a way Lulie Westfeldt's book is a genuine tribute to the Technique, because whilst she clearly did not like the man she derived great benefit from the principle, which implies that a distinction can be drawn between the man and his discovery.

I've often experienced that if someone does something for another person and the latter feels a tremendous sense of obligation, then there is almost inevitably a subconscious reaction to seize the first opportunity to do them down. Indeed, I always advise the students on the training course that it is very important when they become teachers not to let their pupils feel a strong sense of obligation. As long as they are able to feel that they can reciprocate everything works beautifully. But if a sense of indebtedness builds up, things are apt to go wrong.

This is recognised by a large number of practitioners in the caring professions from psychotherapists to social workers, and junior teachers should be particularly careful about people to whom they give concessions in their fees – if they give free lessons for instance. It's best for the teacher to dream up some odd jobs so the pupils can feel they're paying their way. Lulie undoubtedly felt a tremendous sense of obligation to FM and one can understand why; he'd done for her what no one else had been able to do.

But I don't agree with you that it is possible to draw a distinction between FM and the Technique. As we said earlier, without the man there would have been no Technique. I remember that

Ethel Webb, FM's secretary, used to say that there was only one Alexander Technique, and that was the technique taught by FM Alexander: in so far as the rest of us taught it, we weren't really teaching the same technique. I'd agree with that to a certain extent.

In what sense?

Well, FM always emphasised the artistic aspect of the Technique. I think FM could quite reasonably be described as an artist and craftsman. And in all such work, the stamp of the individual is there. This is how, for example, an art historian can look at a picture and say, "Yes, this is a genuine Rembrandt, but this one most certainly isn't," or whatever. In fact, as far as the Technique is concerned, it goes a little further than that. What needs to be borne in mind is that FM is the only person we know of who worked out the Technique in order to correct his own standard of sensory appreciation. All the rest of us have learned it from somebody whose hands have helped and guided us. So obviously there is a difference between how Alexander taught himself the Technique and how everyone else has learned it. You could say there was something unique in his teaching because he had unique knowledge of it.

You told me once that Alexander was, by nature, a suspicious man. Can you say a bit more about this aspect of his personality?

Yes, until he got to know someone he was watchful and very reserved. He was always on the look-out for people who would try and do him down. I remember one night he took me to a restaurant and they brought a bottle of wine without the cork. FM sent it straight back, because he was convinced that they'd filled it from a cask in the cellar. He made a tremendous fuss about it, much to my embarrassment.

Does that watchfulness explain the episode when he demanded to see Moshe Feldenkrais – the founder of the Feldenkrais

Method – upon finding out that he was having a course of lessons with you at Ashley Place?

Oh yes, and with good reason. After all, Feldenkrais' book, *Body and Mature Behaviour*,* has a lot of material in it that looks as though it is practically paraphrased from Alexander's books. When FM realised that Feldenkrais was having lessons, he naturally wanted to see him to find out what reasons he had for coming when he'd written this book and developed his own method. It was perfectly clear by implication that Alexander was accusing him of seeking to plagiarise further by taking more lessons. FM was sensitive about anything that could be regarded as plagiarism and, once again, with good reason – because even in the early days he'd had bad experiences with people who'd tried to pass off his work as their own. I also suspect – though this is only a guess – that he'd met a lot of "wide-boys" when he first went to Melbourne after leaving his job at the Mount Bischoff tin mine in Tasmania. There were lots of small-time con men in the big metropolis just waiting for innocent, wide-eyed country boys whom they could exploit. No doubt FM had had some experience of these characters in the past.

So what actually happened when Alexander and Feldenkrais met each other: did they talk for a long time or just for a few minutes?

Oh, just for a few minutes. Alexander had Feldenkrais's book with him and told him that he'd read it and wanted to know why he had come for lessons. He said that if he didn't receive a satisfactory answer he could have no more lessons. Well, Feldenkrais was left absolutely speechless – he didn't have a word to say – and that was it. He was ushered out.

You met Feldenkrais again, didn't you?

Yes, I met him in Copenhagen in 1959. It was at a Congress organised by Gerda Alexander. She'd managed to get the Danish

---

* Moshe Feldenkrais *Body and Mature Behaviour* (1949).

Ministry of Education to set up and finance the event. Many people from what these days would be called "bodywork" were invited. So there were dancers, physiotherapists, Alexander people – Frank Pierce Jones, for example, was a principal speaker – Feldenkrais and representatives of Gerda Alexander's own subject, eutony, giving lectures and workshops.

Did Feldenkrais recognise you?

Oh, yes! When he came in to give his first lecture, he found me in the front row. He did a sort of double-take.

He explained his methods presumably?

Yes, there were about a hundred people in attendance in the workshop I attended in the second week – the first week was given over to lectures – and Feldenkrais introduced us to his system: "Awareness through Movement", which involved sitting or lying – lying mostly – and exploring various movements. They were very similar sorts of exercises to those outlined by Raymond Dart, where, say, in order to extend the range of vision with head turning, you close the left eye and look to the left with the right eye. By doing this a few times it's possible to extend the range of movement. The neuro-physiology behind this is that the leading eye generates inhibitory messages to the antagonistic neck muscles which gets more freedom, facilitating a wider turning circle. Feldenkrais utilised similar principles and it was possible to get an increased range of movement in the arms, legs and so on outside people's habitual range. It was creating a change in the reflex mechanisms, in short. But, as far as I know, this facilitation doesn't have any practical application. It certainly doesn't have any relevance for the Alexander Technique.

Still, I assume that if you spent half-an-hour on the floor stimulating various reflex patterns and increasing the habitual range of movement, there would be some change, albeit temporary, in terms of overall movement when you were upright again, wouldn't there?

Yes, that's right. I would think acrobats and some dancers might find the procedures useful, although many of them would have experienced something like that in their training in any case.

Feldenkrais's work has been applied to running by one of his students, Jack Heggie.* Heggie emphasises the spiralic nature of the movement process in general, and in running in particular, and recommends various sitting and floor exercises, with the intention that the runner pre-sets the nervous system. The basic idea is that when the runner gets off the floor and starts running he or she will run in a different and more efficient way. Do you think that's plausible?

Well, in the matter of running, it's perfectly true that you can practise and get the contra-rotations of the pelvis and shoulders needed in good running. But what does all this have to do with habit? That's the thing. When people come to do anything in the ordinary way, they do it according to what feels right and natural. It means, of course, that you can cultivate misuse just as readily – even more so, really – as good use. It's the old, old problem – the problem of habitual response – which FM highlighted in "Evolution of a Technique" in *The Use of the Self*. As I mentioned previously, the basic thing in running is to ensure that the neck is free, allowing the head to go forward and up, thus maintaining the lengthening and not the shortening of stature. That's really what it is all about.

You're saying, in effect, that with improved use the various spiralic movements and contra-rotations happen anyway. There's no need to "do" or practise them in any way.

That's quite correct.

Did FM express any opinion about whether the Technique would spread or wasn't he particularly bothered about such issues?

---

* Jack Heggie *Running with the Whole Body* (1986).

It's difficult to know what his opinion was towards the end of his life. I think he hoped it would spread, just as he hoped that a 100–1 shot would win the Derby or St Leger. But I don't think he had great confidence that it would spread, and he was disillusioned about most of the people who had worked with him. As he saw it, there were only a few of us in whom he had confidence. But, there again, I don't know what his real thoughts were about my prospects and capabilities, for example. He must have thought that I had some capability or he wouldn't have asked me to give up my teaching in Oxford and help run the training course. And clearly he thought Margaret Goldie would do the best she could, and that was why he made her co-trustee of his estate.

So would you say he was pessimistic?

I think he must have been. It must have been sad for him that after all the battles of a long life he couldn't feel any great confidence that his work would be carried on.

So what was the level of interest in the Technique when Alexander died?

Well, there were still people interested in training and having lessons. But I can recall saying to the members of STAT in 1964 or thereabouts that I thought we should give the whole thing another ten years and if, in that time, there hadn't been some major progress – if it wasn't catching on by that time – then what was likely to happen was that the Technique would fade out, not least because the senior teachers were all getting older and were likely to lose enthusiasm. Of course, that didn't happen. One thing, in particular, that helped in this country was that the then London County Council, followed by its successor institution, the Greater London Council, agreed to give grants for students to train. And there were a lot of social and cultural changes happening at the time. The 1960s – the so-called "swinging sixties" – meant that a lot of people became less conventional in their attitudes and behaviour. Certainly, people became more ready to look at alternative medicine and, although we've always pointed out that we weren't in the therapy business, we were, nonetheless, an alternative approach to health problems and, indeed, lots of other problems.

The thing is that, in Alexander's early days, not very many people knew about the Technique. Initially, it was mainly recommended by doctors to some of their patients. Then those same people often told their friends and relatives about it. The general perception was that the Technique was cranky and unconventional, when to be unconventional was considered to be a fairly serious criticism. So overall it's very much the case that attitudes have changed – people are now more open-minded and willing to try something new – and it's changed in our favour.

Nowadays, the Alexander Technique has gained a reputation for the management of "bad" backs. In fact, the "bad" back seems to be endemic in western society: only something like 10% of the population have never experienced or never will experience back pain. It's second only to the common cold for people to seek medical advice. Have back problems always been a reason why people sought out the Alexander Technique?

No, I wouldn't say so. In the past, people mainly came through breathing difficulties. It's only in recent years that there's been this focus on back pain and, to some extent, this is because a great many Alexander teachers don't really know much about breathing and they haven't considered breathing and voice in the way Alexander did.

Can you elaborate?

Well, voice and breathing are a lot less ambiguous than anything to do with back pain. When it comes to how you breathe, the problem is clear and straightforward. For example, are you breathing through the nose or are you breathing through the mouth? This is a very simple but also very conclusive test. It's easy for people to miss the point that one of the main effects of pulling the head back is that you breathe through the mouth. It's very difficult to breathe through the nose if the head's pulled back.

In fact, compared to breathing, back pain isn't a simple matter at all. For example, MRI scans, which provide very clear pictures of the spine, spinal cord and discs, have proved, unfortunately, to be less helpful to the medical profession than was once hoped, because of an interesting asymmetry: some people with severe backache produce relatively normal scans, whilst some people with highly abnormal scans have no problems at all.

That's perfectly true. It's one of the reasons why some medical experts have proposed that the major cause of back pain lies in the facet joints and they're too small to show up. And I think that proposition is probably quite right. People forget the importance of the facet joints: when you stiffen and pull down it's the facet joints that are affected immediately.

So how do you assess this contemporary association of the Technique with the alleviation and management of back pain? Is it dangerous, or what?

I don't think it's dangerous or anything like that, but it may mislead people and make them overlook much more important matters. The fact is there's a big public demand for something that will help back pain and, yes, the Technique will help back pain.

Although a lot of research has been carried out into the variety and causes of back pain, what's always neglected is whether in the activity of living – in movement – pressure is being put on or off the joints. It must be a matter of common-sense that, when you move, it's better to take pressure off rather than put it on the joints. That's an elementary mechanical principle but one that's easily forgotten. And it is a principle that we promote. Having said that, there are lots of causes of back pain that we can't possibly deal with. Take someone with ankylosing spondylitis. Now, no amount of inhibiting and directing is going to affect the pathology of this condition and its basic, fundamental cause, which, in any case, remains obscure. On the other hand, if someone's got ankylosing spondylitis, then it's certainly to their advantage to study and observe their movement patterns so that, when they go to move, they take the pressure off the joints as much as possible.

The Alexander Technique had been fashionable before – in the 1930s for example – and interest then subsided. We now seem to be in another period of interest: do you think there's any danger in these fashions, is it to be welcomed, or is it simply just part of the social landscape?

I think it's very much part of the landscape. The previous waves of interest always came to an untimely end that had nothing to do with the Technique but rather with world events – namely the two world wars. But clearly the danger to anything that gets popular and expands is that demand can rapidly outstrip supply and in our case you'll find people teaching the Technique who are not properly qualified and give it a bad name, particularly in the USA. Even people who are properly qualified can be tempted to dilute it for mass consumption. As I said earlier, Alexander during his lifetime thought it essential that he should succeed in producing benefit for anyone who came to him for lessons, or else there had to be an extremely good explanation of why it didn't work. He realised that his own credibility and that of the Technique were on the line. Nowadays none of us feels under the same pressure, because it's possible to say of someone who has lessons that don't work out: "Well, it's unfortunate, but it's not real evidence that the Technique's no good, because lots of other people have benefited." I also think that some teachers are not as concerned for the reputation of the Technique and their own teaching practice as they ought to be. I've even come across teachers who've claimed to have been teaching for ten years, but you find that in fact they've been teaching fewer than fifteen lessons a week and considering that a lot of work! I consider fifteen lessons a day or its equivalent one normal day's work, and anybody who's doing substantially less than that is really just playing at it. Of course, I recognise that when people first begin teaching, something like four lessons a day may be as much as they can manage. I remember that after I'd been teaching a little while and then had to take eight pupils in a day I found it quite an effort. But as time passed, I was able to increase the number until I could regularly take fourteen or fifteen pupils a day. At times I've taken eighteen pupils a day, to see if I could manage the same number that FM did when he was living in New York during the First World War. It's interesting to note that FM found that number the limit and, from my experience, I'd certainly agree with him.

Why did Alexander take that number of people?

I think he was trying to establish the Technique and he needed the money. At that time, private teaching was the only way he could make a living. But this very definitely isn't a career in which you can expect to make money. One ought to be able to make a reasonable living and pay one's way, but that's about it. It's the same with a career in the National Health Service, for instance. If you go into it intending to make money as you might in business or industry, it means that things won't work out. You're likely to get very disillusioned.

You clearly define teaching the Technique in vocational terms.

Yes, I do. I think you've got to see it in vocational terms or, at any rate, as something you enjoy doing. The rewards really revolve around job satisfaction, in my opinion. If an Alexander teacher doesn't derive much satisfaction from the work, perhaps they'd be better off doing something else.

In contemporary society, there are any number of body–mind therapies and disciplines. How should the Technique define itself in this milieu? Should it even attempt to? Should it, perhaps, just get on and plough its own furrow?

I think the Technique has to plough its own furrow. Very definitely. As you rightly point out, there are a great number of body–mind disciplines and practices around but, in actual fact, nearly all of them are based on the principles of separation of the organism, even though their advocates may formally deny this and stake a claim to holism, mind–body unity and so on. To my knowledge, the only people who have any inkling of mind–body unity are the biofeedback people. An integral part of their work is the recognition that thought processes generate action potential in the muscles. But mind–body unity was fundamental to Alexander's whole approach. It's often said that Alexander was wrong when he refused to co-operate with any scientific analysis of the Technique which would have validated his work. But the reason he didn't was that his knowledge of scientists led him to conclude that they worked on the principle of separation. They didn't have an understanding of mind–body unity. So any formal tests they set up were bound to be flawed.

From what you've already said, I take it that you're not too keen on combining the Alexander Technique with other disciplines which to many people might look as if they inhabit the same or similar sort of cultural space?

No, I don't think you can. Let's take something like psychotherapy. Now my direct experience of it is very limited, but my observation of its effects on people who are trying to deal with depression, anxiety or whatever is that it isn't very successful.

Why?

Because you're not going to deal with people's problems by utilising procedures that fail to take into account the working of the organism as a whole. Undoubtedly, you will find people who will claim that psychoanalysis or whatever relieves their depression, but it has to be recognised that "cure" can be obtained by transfer. So often a condition can be helped or relieved at the expense of something else.

In any case, you're quite sceptical about talking cures, aren't you?

Yes.

On what grounds – that it's possible endlessly to verbalise?

Yes, you can certainly do that. And on the grounds that talking cures don't address the problems of basic mechanisms. The strength of Alexander's approach was that he addressed the problems of elementary mechanics. As he stood in front of the mirror to find out what was causing his hoarseness, he recognised that there were certain things wrong from a mechanical point of view. He found that if the neck is stiffened and the head is pulled back, the chest raised and the back hollowed, the whole structure is distorted and it makes the ability to balance on two legs with lightness and freedom that much more difficult. Now, even people with deep emotional problems have to recognise that they've got to breathe, have a working digestion and an efficient circulatory system. If the postural machinery is not working well, the other machinery will not work well either.

You don't think that people need to deal first with these issues and somehow get them out of the way?

But why do they need to deal with them? I don't see any reason why they have to – it's all water under the bridge. I'd say the sooner it's forgotten the better. You consciously put it into perspective.

And the dominant perspective should be everyday life in the here and now – "thinking in activity", to use John Dewey's apt phrase?

That's right.

At a practical level, then, how do you respond when pupils or students voice their anxieties? For example, what do you do in a lesson if someone starts telling you about their awful childhood?

Well, you're not there to discuss their awful childhood. The teacher is there to give a lesson and should be dealing with whether the person is stiffening the neck and pulling themselves down in that particular moment. Teaching the Technique is very much a question of staying in the present, and delving into the past is none of the teacher's business. Having said that, anyone can express anything they like, so long as they go up to do it. It's when they start pulling down and interfering with the basic mechanics that they're in trouble. That's the thing.

I'd like now to return to the historical context: did you have much contact with FM's brother, A. R. Alexander?

I had a certain amount of contact with him. I first met him shortly after I'd joined the training course, but he was about to go back to Boston to teach. The people on the first training course had much more contact with him because he'd been around for quite a lot of the time. He came back to England once a year and visited the training course. He had a house in Sidcup, and because I was friendly with Max and Marjory, his son and niece, I used to see him there. He was also in England for six months before his death in 1949, and used to come into Ashley Place. Overall I didn't know him very well, although I did work with him from time to time.

How did he differ from his brother?

The main difference during the period when I knew him was that he was severely handicapped by the spinal fracture he received after being thrown from his horse. He used a cane, and walking, standing and sitting were all difficult for him. He was a strong character – a very strong personality. I think that, just as FM wouldn't have gone unnoticed in a crowd, neither would AR. He did, however, have to adopt a different approach to teaching than FM because of the handicap. You remember FM's famous statement: "Now, I can give it to them whether they like it or not!"?

Yes.

Well, I don't think AR would ever have said that, because he was much more dependent on the pupil's co-operation – their thought and attention. Compared to FM, he was much more demanding. In fact, FM in his last years worked quite quietly.

Would you say that there was any advantage in AR's approach – or would it differ from one individual to another?

It differed from one individual to another, which is true of teaching overall. Almost anybody will benefit from having lessons from different teachers. Often people are not the best judges of who is the best teacher for them. It doesn't follow that someone you like and with whom you have a nice, cosy relationship is the person from whom you'll learn the most. You can often learn a lot from people you don't get on with at all – even from someone you heartily dislike.

Did he sit while teaching?

Yes, he sat on a stool. He didn't sit beside but in front of you. Although he used his hands, he also used his eyes. And he watched your eyes and facial expression and it was in that way he could tell whether you were inhibiting and directing.

But he could take people in and out of the chair perfectly well from a sitting position. And, of course, FM used to sit a lot too: he always had a stool for himself as part of his standard equipment. He used it when taking someone's legs or working on whispered "ahs", for instance. AR also often worked on people in lying down.

On a table?

No, on the floor. He'd pull his stool up and lean over the pupil.

How did the two brothers get on; earlier you indicated that there was sometimes a bit of friction between them?

Like a lot of siblings, there was some antagonism at a superficial level, but at a deeper level they got on extremely well. Although they sometimes argued and quarrelled between themselves, they immediately closed ranks if attacked by outsiders. It was often said that one of the reasons AR went to America was because he found teaching at Ashley Place increasingly difficult. Some people on the training course delighted in setting the two brothers against each other. I think Lulie Westfeldt says something to that effect in her book. But I think the real reason was that only by going to America could AR make a reasonable living, although I should point out that neither AR nor FM were in any sense wealthy men.

Is it true that FM had shown AR the Technique in six lessons?

I don't think anyone knows really; it's entirely speculation. I knew Max, AR's son, well and he didn't know anything about it. No one knows how the two brothers came to work together in Melbourne. But come together they did, because when FM moved to Sydney, AR remained behind and took over the practice. Then AR joined FM in Sydney, and when FM came to London in 1904, AR continued giving lessons in Sydney until 1909, when he too came to London. They worked together – presumably harmoniously – until FM decided to go to the USA in 1914 when, once again, AR continued the practice in England. So overall they were used to working together and taking each other's pupils. But, as I say, nobody knows how AR got started. The only time that anyone knows that AR got any work from FM was immediately after the riding accident when he received a spinal fracture. But this was 1924, and AR must have been teaching for at least twenty years at that point.

So you never saw the two brothers working on each other, say, on the training course?

No, never. But I'm sure they must have talked and discussed things. And, of course, AR did work on the training course with FM, so he must have picked up a tremendous amount. And AR read the books, so altogether he really did know what it was all about.

PART III

It's clear that your approach to teaching the Technique is kept nice and simple: it largely revolves around chair work. Why do you favour this approach?

Well, first of all let me say that I agree with Alexander that a teacher should try to give every lesson as if it were a first lesson. That way one's approach is always fresh, because one is disregarding what has happened in the previous lesson. I also mentioned previously, but it's worth repeating, that FM used to say that there's no set of exercises for people to go and practise – "sitting" and "standing" and things like that – but that he was teaching something that can be put into practice from the moment the pupil goes out of the door at the end of a lesson. So if a teacher can get the pupil to use the chair a bit better, it's an important way through which to learn about inhibition and direction. As we also discussed previously, FM didn't limit himself to the chair, nor did he consider that others should do so: it all depends on the pupil's problems, what their interests are, how many lessons they've had, and so on.

So, it's entirely reasonable to give people lessons from the point of view of their practical interests. But one also has to remember that beginners who come for a basic course of thirty lessons have to be introduced to the basic principles of the Technique. One runs the risk, therefore, by doing a little bit of this and then a bit of that – say, creeping one day, writing the next, dancing the day after, varying the contents of the lessons all the time – that pupils will merely look upon what you do with them as a sort of variety act. This will only serve to obscure the fundamental principles involved in the Technique, and instead they'll merely go away thinking: "Yes, I see. I do this like this and that like that." So it is important to have a situation that is very simple, where the problem is clear and can be addressed in a straightforward way, and where repetition can be used in a highly constructive way. Then, of course, one can move on to other things.

In your initial interview with the pupil what do you try and find out? Additionally, what do you try and convey?

I get the pupil to explain why they've come and what they know or don't know about the Technique. For example, the other day a young woman came for an interview and she told me she'd been recommended to come by her doctor because of an ongoing painful back. So having established that, I said to her, as I would say to anyone: "Now, let me show you what we do and then we can discuss it afterwards." I get the pupil to stand in front of the chair and look out of the window, and explain that the purpose of looking out is that they don't have any plans to do anything else. This means that the automatic functioning of the body – the breathing, digestion and especially the balance mechanisms are working as well as they can without any conscious intervention or interference on their part. They're not trying to do anything, in other words. So when they've accepted that, I explain that, with their consent, I'm going to put my hands on them – I take their head or whatever – and point out that as they let go, they're growing and going up to their full height and are then more free. I might, additionally, point out the consequences – they're breathing more, for example. Now, depending how well they respond I might go on to point out that the real problem is the problem of reaction: if you're asked to do something, the normal response is to do it, and then it's done in an habitual way, and so on.

Do you ever ask the pupil to sit and stand without your help so you can observe them first? Do you, perhaps, then imitate their

movement pattern, so they can see for themselves what they're doing?

No, I certainly don't. How they sit and stand is likely to be awful in any case and the less they're encouraged to do awful things the better. There's no point to my mind in asking someone to do something wrong when, instead, you can get them to leave themselves alone and immediately introduce them to a new and better experience. The whole fundamental principle of the Technique is to get people to stop doing things. As for imitating their movement, I don't see the point of that at all. As FM used to say: "Imitation is the poorest form of learning."

So overall you're immediately putting the emphasis on inhibition rather than performance?

Absolutely. You're not asking the pupil to perform or teach them different things: you're trying to teach them not to do.

When people first come across the Alexander Technique and the use of the chair, they often tend to assume that this is the way they should always sit. They then try and "do" it. One consequence of this is that people become almost afraid to use the back of the chair for support and rest. In short, it can lead to some very strange behaviour. Perhaps you could clarify matters.

I explain this to people in the initial interview as I give them a demonstration using the chair. When I finish I say, "Of course, you're not going to sit like that. Sit back in the chair and make yourself comfortable." I always point out that there's a clear difference between the requirements of "active" as opposed to "restful" sitting. "Active" sitting is the attitude you adopt when you're going to do anything like play the piano, use a word-processor, ride a horse or, indeed, have an Alexander lesson. "Restful" sitting, on the other hand, is how you sit when reading, watching the television and so on. It's sensible to take advantage of the support of the chair and in that way breathing, circulation and digestion – your general functioning – is able to tick over without interference and your neuro-muscular system doesn't have to work overtime to keep you in balance.

How much information do you require of their medical conditions and problems?

I always ask about their medical situation. I then try and make sure they're seeing someone. I make it clear, however, that it's not my business to tell them who to go to – whether they go to a homoeopath, herbalist or conventional doctor is their decision – but they should get professional advice because that isn't my department.

How do you make it clear to the pupil that the Alexander Technique is not a therapy, particularly to those who've been on a Cook's Tour of conventional and alternative therapies and think that this is just another port of call?

If anyone comes to me and says that they've got this, that or the other, I say, "Well, alright. But the fact of the matter is that the way you use yourself – the way you stiffen, pull down and fail to breathe – will inevitably make whatever you've got worse than it needs to be. In any case, a diagnosis is never 100% – it's impossible to be absolutely sure what the conditions really are until you give the Technique a try and learn to use yourself better. If you can get an improvement in use and general functioning then, hopefully, it will become clearer what the real problem is. We don't necessarily have to accept that the problem is as stated." I find it's worth taking time to get people to see that, and very often, if they do, it's that change in attitude that leads to good results. If the teacher leaves the pupil under any impression that they're giving treatment or trying to relieve symptoms, it's probably going to cause trouble. In these situations, when somebody came in and said to FM that they had ankylosing spondylitis or whatever, he'd say, "If your doctor says that's what you've got, then that's probably what you've got. But I don't know anything about that. What I do know is that you're not breathing and you're stiffening the neck and pulling the head back."

So Alexander never attempted to usurp or take on the rôle of the doctor by offering or formulating a quasi-medical diagnosis?

Definitely not. In fact, FM would always deny knowledge even when he had knowledge.

How do you deal with people in acute pain?

You just carry on – there's nothing else you can do really. Obviously, as I said before, you enquire what other treatment they're having, but if they're in a lot of pain and taking lots of sedatives or pain-killers it's often pretty useless working on them because their sensitivity is dull – they're doped and it's very difficult to work on someone who's anaesthetised in that way.

Have you found that increasing age is a barrier to learning?

Not necessarily. I think you can have problems with all ages.

The Alexander Technique is concerned with growth or change, but perhaps you can clarify what sort of change we are talking about?

Well, there's no formal doctrine of change. At one level, the type of change depends entirely upon the individual. At another level, the type of change comes under the heading "general functioning". Now, people might say that the term "general functioning" is extremely vague, and I suppose it is. For example, we're not even going to claim that we're going to improve someone's blood pressure, the workings of the heart or, indeed, any sort of specific change that might be measured. I think as soon as you start predicting change, you can get into very deep waters. However, it's a matter of common-sense that if you can get people to move more lightly and freely – so that they're taking pressure off rather than putting it on – it must be beneficial. And I think it's quite widely recognised, even in circles outside the Alexander Technique, that if you can get people to think about what they're doing, what they're going to do and so on, rather than behave thoughtlessly, it's generally a better way of going about things.

So what do you think can be achieved by a course of, say, thirty lessons from a competent teacher?

I think someone can learn enough of the ABC of the Technique so that, even if they never have any more lessons, they'll have taken something away that will have made a change in and a valuable contribution to their lives. At the very least, they've got a rudimentary idea about inhibition and direction. But I think if you have much less than thirty lessons, you can't be sure that this will be so. I always emphasise that even twenty-eight lessons isn't good enough. Certainly, I've known people who've had twenty-eight lessons and you don't seem to be getting any response at all, and then the "Road to Damascus" experience takes place on the twenty-ninth lesson. So I always say to prospective pupils that if they're going to do it at all, they need to make a commitment to thirty lessons. They may well have more, but the practical point is not to have less. As I mentioned earlier, I also emphasise that when they start they need lessons as frequently as possible: ideally, they should come every day for three weeks or so, but very often if this isn't practical then three lessons a week will do. But the absolute minimum is once a week. And I explain to the pupil that if they choose the latter course, they're giving themselves the least favourable chance to learn, even though we'll try and make the best of it.

Do you give a new pupil any sort of prediction about what the future might hold?

Not in those sorts of terms. If someone comes with a speech or breathing problem I might say, "Well, considering how fixed your ribcage is, it's not surprising." But then I say, "What changes can be made – what the results will be – are just something that we'll have to wait and see." I tell people that you can't predict what the outcome will be. But you've got to give it a go to find out. The phrase FM constantly used to a new pupil in this context was: "Yes, I think you can be helped." Note, he didn't say, "I think I can help you." Really, that's quite a difference. And it was a very deliberate choice of words. What FM wanted to get across was that the person could be helped, if they showed any willingness to help themselves.

Did Alexander ever refuse to take somebody on? Did he ever say to someone, "Look, to be honest, I don't think you can be helped"?

I never knew him to refuse someone: and for the reason he used to say, "You don't know until you try."

You don't routinely or automatically use the table in teaching, do you?

It depends entirely on the pupil. I do use the table a reasonable amount. And, certainly, with new pupils I always make a point of putting them on the table at some point in the first few lessons in order to explain lying down. After that it very much depends on their particular condition. If I can get what I want with them in standing and sitting they can do their lying down for themselves at home or wherever. It's only if I can't get what I want – if they're tired or something – that I'll put them on the table.

I assume that it's not a useful idea for a teacher to keep exclusively to the table?

Again, it depends on the pupil and what their problems are but, in general, you are trying to give them something to put into practice. And no matter how much they might like to do so, they can't spend all their time lying on their backs.

How do you deal with people who often have very vigorous and rigorous training regimes like dancers and sports people?

I tend to do more table-work in the beginning because they're the type of people who won't be used to leaving themselves alone. By doing table-work in the early stages it's possible to overcome the tendency to "do" to a degree. I also try and get across that the Technique is something contrary to their habit and experience, even if sometimes that's not very acceptable.

I remember that you once told me that sports people in particular can get worried or anxious if they're not fulfilling their daily or weekly quota of exercise.

That's right. I always take it from lesson to lesson and hope that, as a pupil becomes more aware of what the problem is – how every time they go to get out of the chair they stiffen the neck and pull the head back – it will gradually dawn on them that they do the same thing when they do all the other things in their life.

The terrible truth reveals itself?

That's right. But the important point is that the truth has to reveal itself to them. The best a teacher can do is to give them the opportunity to learn that lesson and hope that the penny will drop.

And if it doesn't drop?

There's nothing you can do about it. You can only do your best. Take my mother as an example: there was a woman spending eighteen out of twenty-four hours in bed, and the two basic things she had to learn were how to lie down in semi-supine and get straightened out, and how to sit in a chair without doing herself great harm. FM found it was possible to show her these things, and after that she was on the road. But, if that hadn't been possible, what could FM, or any other teacher for that matter, have done?

Do you check to see whether people are regularly lying in semi-supine?

Yes, I do.

How do you explain the purpose and practice of lying down to pupils?

I explain it very much as FM used to explain it: that people in the course of their daily activities get pulled down, shortened and out of shape but that lying down creates expansion and puts them into a better shape. The main aspect of lying down is to leave yourself alone – not to make muscular effort in other words – while, as usual, making sure that the neck is not stiffening, the head is going forward and up, so that the back can lengthen and widen and the knees can go up to the ceiling. You've got these four main areas to think about. And that's quite a lot really. Of course, when people lie down initially, they're often so fixed that they don't feel what's happening, but then as things let go they might feel a twist or something and be tempted to make some sort of adjustment. If they come and tell me about it, I tell them not to do anything. I just say: "That's fine. If you feel it, ignore it!" Lying down is very much about non-doing. You lie down not to do.

Additionally, do you explain that it's useful to think about the weight-bearing points – occiput, scapulae, hip bones and feet – in semi-supine?

Yes, I sometimes do. If you're lying on a hard surface and you know about the weight-bearing points – you've got an experience of them, in other words – then you can include in your directions the idea that you're going to let each part take its due bit of weight. Of course, with all these things it's often quite tricky, because you're so dependent on feeling to know what's happening and it's easy to get so involved in feelings that you forget to direct. So you have to be careful. The other thing I emphasise to pupils is that the less strain made in getting down to semi-supine, the less damage there is to undo on arrival. Similarly, in getting up, the more freely the return to upright, the greater the benefit in terms of release and getting into a better shape.

What attitude should the legs and arms take?

The feet should be as comfortably and conveniently close to the pelvis as possible. But you don't want them so close that you're making muscular effort. In particular, you don't want the hamstrings to be tight.

And if they are? Do you move the legs?

Try directing the knees to the ceiling and see if you can release them in that way before attempting any movement. As for the arms, the main thing you're looking for is the effect on the shoulders. It's very important to have the shoulders free and opening out. And there's no doubt that different attitudes and positions of the arms will influence the shoulders. For example, some people find it very uncomfortable to have the arms and hands by the sides supported by the floor. In that case, it's much better that they put the hands on the ribcage and get some support.

What about the use of eyes?

This is an important part. The first consideration is to look out and not let the eyes go out of focus – the point is not to stare but to let the eyes focus on different objects. If the eyes do go out of focus, all the eye muscles go slack and that is not in keeping with what you really want to happen. It's important that people realise that they don't lie down for a rest or a sleep. I tell pupils that if they're so tired that they need to sleep they're better off lying down on the sofa or bed and having a proper sleep. Lying down as we teach it is a procedure to correct the consequences of habitual misdirection and to get into better shape.

And the breathing?

Well, when you're lying down and have got everything going satisfactorily, then you've got a very good opportunity to perform some whispered "ahs".

And what do you say to pupils who say they find it difficult to find the time to lie down?

I just say that they can do it either first thing in the morning or last thing at night, if they can't find any other time.

People – particularly new pupils – often ask what they can do between lessons. So what advice do you give them?

I always say that, firstly, they can lie down and, secondly, that if they're to put the Technique into practice straight away they want to apply it to something quite specific. I normally suggest that they focus on sitting down and standing up and try to say "No" and pause before either activity is attempted. I explain that the technique of stopping can be applied to everything. But things that can be applied to everything very easily end up being applied to nothing. So I advise them to play sitting and standing as a game and see how many times they can remember to stop before the activity and how many times they just forget all about it. I say, "You know, you can amuse yourself by keeping the score. Every time you remember, then it's one for you, and every time you forget then it's one for the opposition." Now, I've said this to some very intelligent and serious-minded people over the years and you might expect that they'd consider such an approach to be too childish, but they've taken to it like ducks to water. They burst into the room at the next lesson and say something like: "Do you know, that thing you told me to do is harder than I thought. But I managed to remember ten times." So this method is a good practical way into the problem.

Initially, therefore, you're not so much concerned with direction but inhibition?

That's right. All they need to do is stop, that's all. The rest can follow as and when appropriate.

Do you explain that they're not meant to stiffen to pause?

Yes, certainly. You've got to make it very clear in the lesson that you've both been working to free the breathing and get lightness and freedom throughout the body and now that they're going to do something – they're going to move, for example – they pause to reinforce the freedom and going up. And it's certainly worth pointing out to pupils that in many athletic disciplines, for instance, the competitors – whether they're throwing the javelin or performing the high, long or triple jump – pause to get themselves in the best psychophysical state they know how to, before going into action. The pause is particularly noticeable with divers: they always have a period of quietness and stillness before they perform. In the Technique, we're trying to get a similar sort of thing going.

How do you convey the reality of direction to pupils?

I think this is where the work with the chair is particularly useful. In stand to sit and sit to stand, the upward direction is very necessary and obvious. Once you've established the inhibition, it's the direction that determines whether it works well or not. Put simply, direction means not pulling the head back, but rather directing it in the opposite direction to backwards and down. And, of course, the concept of direction is a familiar one even to people who walk down the street, drive a car or ride a bicycle. It's all a matter of deciding where you intend to go and then seeing that you get there. You simply monitor the situation to make sure it works out alright.

You need a clear and consistent intention, in other words. You don't want to get distracted half-way through something?

No you don't. It's the same as if you walk out of here to go to Holland Park underground station. You know the direction you've got to go in, you decide you will go and all that's then necessary is to keep the intention sufficiently in mind that you don't forget what you're doing.

You don't encourage your pupils to place the palm of one of their hands at the base of their skull to monitor the head poise when they sit and stand outside lessons, do you?

No. I think that's a very difficult thing to do. In fact, anyone who needs to do that would be very likely to pull the head back when they put the hand on the neck and head. And, once again, it's all based on the attempt to try and feel it out. But with the Technique you're not aiming to be dependent on feeling but instead on thought and direction. In fact, this is where a mirror comes in useful. If you're standing in front of a mirror and directing your head, you can see whether you're pulling it back or not. You don't need to put a hand up to feel it – feeling doesn't even come into it. It's what you see that counts. And, of course, the direction that you give in front of the mirror still has to be given even when the mirror isn't there. The trick is to direct in the same way without the mirror as you do with the mirror. But people tend not to do that: they direct quite happily in front of the mirror and then, after the withdrawal of the mirror, they go back to feeling. And that's very understandable. After all, it's what FM did: he gives a full and frank account of the problem in "Evolution of a Technique".*

Within the context of an introductory course of thirty lessons, are all your pupils introduced to practices like "monkey" and the whispered "ah"?

I certainly do. After all, the whole purpose of what we're doing is to try to free the breathing and get it working properly. Now, whether you actually do textbook whispered "ahs" depends upon the situation, but at some stage you want to introduce pupils to the idea of breathing out rather than breathing in. So you might get people to blow through the lips or do some variation of the "ah" – saying it without worrying too much over the details. I should point out that if you're getting the pupil to perform whispered "ahs" lying down – it's the same as if you try and sing lying down – there's a different muscular set-up than if you're upright. If you expect to get everything the same, it won't happen, simply because there's a difference in the spine and ribcage in the two attitudes. When you're working with the pupil's breathing then it's often very useful to put them in monkey, because coming forward from the hips, if done correctly – this also applies to coming forward in sitting – opens out the thorax. And, of course, in everyday life people will be stooping and bending to pick things up off the floor or whatever. So they certainly need an introduction to that. It's useful in this respect to find out what the pupil's job or

---

* F. M. Alexander *The Use of the Self* (1987)

daily life is like, so you can show them the relevance of monkey to everyday life.

So to sum up your approach in the initial period of lessons: the average human being has quite enough to be getting on with in the simple acts of sitting and standing and a basic introduction to breathing and bending. Is that how you see it?

Yes. Someone's reactions from sit to stand and stand to sit will be habitual and subconscious. That means that the changes a teacher makes will feel wrong and, for some people, be quite disturbing. The teacher's task is to allay nervousness and anxiety, because only then will it be possible to get any sort of rational thinking going. There's a lot to do before people are in much of a state to learn anything, and if they're in pain, that can cause complications too. What you hope to do with your hands is to bring about some change and improvement in the co-ordination. We say that the Alexander Technique is not treatment – but from another point of view it is a sort of treatment; undoubtedly, a strong element of treatment comes into it. One of my favourite stories relates to the comments of one of my sons when he was quite small. He said: "You know, Dad, your work's dead menial". And, of course, he was quite right. You could say that "menial" means doing for other people what they ought to be doing for themselves, so it was a perfectly accurate observation. So there is an element of treatment in the Technique and the teacher has to work in such a way that people get the essential experience. But a teacher must be careful not to say to himself or to others: "Now I'm going to take this person's head forward and up" or "Now I'm going to take this person and lengthen and widen them". Once you think that, you're likely to do something other than work on preventive lines, without the recognition that the right thing does itself. After all, the pupil's head will go forward and up and lengthening and widening will occur naturally if the interference is removed. Thus a teacher doesn't take the head forward and up; he merely removes the interference so that the head goes forward and up.

So it's an error for the teacher to think that it can be "done"?

When you get down to the small print it's difficult to be categorical. A pupil with habitually shortened muscles, for example, requires a tremendous amount of direction to release that shortening and stiffening. So with your hands you are positively stretching and therefore relieving the shortness of the muscles, in order to make it possible for them to operate at a different habitual length. We could reasonably put it this way: it's the nature of muscle to have a certain length, which we might call its isometric length. At this length, the muscle can function and perform its duties without undue shortening, thus maintaining its elasticity and responsiveness. However, that muscle can shorten almost to a point of rigidity and still perform its various functions, but the cost will be high and it will be done extremely inefficiently. Basically we're trying to restore the length and elasticity of the musculature as a whole so that the natural responses of the muscle will be more efficient. We're not doing the work for the muscle, but rather bringing it into a condition where it's more capable of doing its own proper work, by removing the interferences in the system.

I think one of the most puzzling things for people on training courses – it certainly puzzled me – is that one is told about the desirability of acquiring "non-doing" hands and yet, when one works with teachers like yourself or Peggy Williams, the hands seem to be doing quite a bit.

Yes. When people who don't really know talk about "the hands", they tend to think only about the hands. Most people's hands are comparatively stiff and insensitive; they can't feel much with their hands because through gripping and grasping they're very stiff and shortened into a flexed state. Clearly, if one attempts to do things with the hands in that condition, the effect is that one feels even less because the hands stiffen and shorten even more. Indeed, if you experience hands like that working on you, they create a disagreeable experience.

So, from a slightly different angle, what is the type of doing that needs to be done by the teacher's hands?

It's not that easy to put into words. But let me put it this way: first of all, the teacher uses his or her hands in order to feel whether the person they're in contact with is either fixed or free, light or heavy. Really, you're assessing the general state of liveliness, vitality – whatever you want to call it – the direction in which the energy is flowing. Now, for the teacher to assess this reliably and sensitively, they've got to be going up themselves – they've got to have the freedom, co-ordination and flow of energy that is necessary to lengthen in stature. I've often said to students that it's a similar situation to when you're on an escalator on the underground. You put your hand on the handrail and you know immediately whether the escalator is travelling at the same speed as the handrail. Similarly, the more the teacher is reliably going up, the more readily they can feel what's going on in the pupil. Then if you discern some fixity or rigidity in the pupil – there's stiffness somewhere – you're going to see whether with your hands you can give a stimulus to release it. If the person's definitely pulling down, it's not a question of taking them up, but instead finding out what's causing the pulling down and then stopping it. Then if you find the energy begins to flow and the person is going up, then with your hands you're not really doing anything; rather, you're in effect just saying: "Yes, that's fine. Come on, let's have some more of that." The teacher simply encourages the pupil to think. The process I'm describing, therefore, is very far removed from anything that's understood as manipulation in the ordinary sense.

So the skill of an Alexander teacher is not really of a manipulative sort, but rather the ability to listen with the hands?

Very much so.

But it takes some time for the hands to acquire that capacity to listen?

Yes, of course. And that's true of a number of things, not just the Alexander Technique. There's a famous story about the pianist Vladimir De Pachmann; although it's terribly corny I've every reason to believe that it's true. He'd given a recital at the Wigmore Hall and played the last piece so superbly that there was a complete hush in the hall as the last notes died away; no one rushed to break the magic by applauding. The old man picked up his hands from the keyboard, looked at them and said: "Thank you my hands. You have done well tonight." A lot of performers have that type of sensitivity. Indeed, FM on occasion used to say: "My hands know more about it than I do."

You've developed the use of your hands to a very high degree. Have there been recognisable stages in that development?

Yes, but I'd find it hard to define them. It's simply a matter of practice, and it's tremendously important to use your hands as much as possible. FM said that if he had six months off without using his hands he'd lose several years of work. I think that's perfectly true, and I wouldn't like to go months without using my hands.

Are there any obvious pitfalls in the use of the hands that are worth indicating?

Well, it would be very easy for someone, having listened to me about non-doing, to become so obsessed with having sensitive hands that they're almost afraid to put them on. They might do it so lightly and delicately that they don't really give themselves a chance to feel anything. In training people to use their hands, I make a great deal of the idea of using the hands as feet. Creeping on the hands and knees as I've already indicated is one valuable way to free the hands and open them out towards hyperextension, which leads to greater sensitivity. I also say to students: "Now put the hands on and don't be afraid of letting the person take the weight of your arms." There's all the difference between pulling down on someone and letting them take your weight. Most people are perfectly capable of absorbing the weight of the arms. I encourage the practice and experience of getting quite a firm touch, and therefore I'm very much against people whose hands flutter about when they're teaching.

Could you say something about the duration of contact made with the hands?

This is a very important area. FM used to say that inexperienced teachers tend to keep their hands on for too long, which is fine as long as you're giving a good stimulus. But unless you're absolutely sure of that, you might be very easily transmitting a poor or even a bad stimulus, without realising you're doing so. To be on the safe side, the rule is: Don't leave your hands on too long. On the other hand, as I've just pointed out, the hands shouldn't flit about like butterflies.

You're also very much against sticking the elbows out whilst teaching. Could you explain why?

Well, from a mechanical point of view this is a symptom of over-use of the deltoid muscles and those of the shoulder-girdle. If you stick the elbows out, you'll almost certainly be creating tension in the neck, because you'll raise the shoulders, and so on. Since the basic idea of the Technique is to achieve freedom with minimum effort, you shouldn't hold the elbows out or move the upper arm away from the sides, unless you've got a very good reason for doing so. And to return to the subject of horse-riding once again: the best riding masters have always appreciated that, to achieve the optimum balance of the body, the arms should be in to the side. As soon as you start moving the arms away, you create extra problems in balance and so you're obliged to make extra muscular effort to compensate.

How much should a teacher be using their eyes, or can it all be done by feel?

Alexander used to say to us, "You've got no excuse for misusing your hands when you can actually see what you're doing with them." He always took it for granted that where you could use your eyes to see, you would use them. That way, you wouldn't simply rely on your feelings.

Now, suppose a teacher is working on a pupil and encounters some stiffening or resistance, how should he or she proceed?

The general rule is that when you run up against a problem of any kind like that, you want to check yourself out first. You've got to make sure you can exonerate yourself first of all, and then you can start looking at the pupil. And, of course, there may be all sorts of reasons why something like that happens. It may have nothing to do with the teacher – they're not giving a bad stimulus or anything – it's just that there's something else that hasn't or can't be observed and taken into account.

But overall skilled use of the hands comes through practice and careful and critical analysis of that practice?

Yes. It should always be borne in mind that the basic questions you're asking of your hands are the same old things: is the pupil going up or down, is the pupil fixed or free? Or, if you like, is this pupil balanced or unbalanced? That's all really.

Do you not think that with all this emphasis on the hands there's a danger of making them into a rather different and special entity?

Yes, that is a danger. It's one of the reasons why, when working with the students, we get them to put hands on according to the relevant circumstances and then emphasise that they need to come back to their own directions. I often tell them that putting the hands on is like putting an electric plug into a socket. You want to make sure there's a proper connection, but once you've got your hands on there you're not concerned with them any longer; you leave them alone because – to return to the analogy – it's not the plug that does the work, but the apparatus attached to the plug. Having said that, it's not an exact analogy, because with a plug connected to an electrical circuit, the energy is flowing one way, whereas in the teaching context it's a two-way flow between teacher and pupil.

It's certainly the case that FM had remarkable hands. Through experience and so on, he developed extremely supple and sensitive hands that were able to make very full contact with the pupil. But his hands – and this is the critical point – were part of what George Coghill called the "total pattern". That's really what a teacher should be aiming for.

I notice that when you're teaching you're very careful not to set up any fear response: you don't reprimand or scold a pupil in any way.

I don't find that reprimanding people is a good way to set about giving a lesson. If someone's holding their leg, for example, they usually know they're doing so, and it's sufficient to point out in a normal way that you don't want them to do that. This should be done without any element of scolding coming into it. If a pupil doesn't know they're holding on to the leg, then it's obvious that there's a blockage or interference that must be worked on. But it can't be worked on if the teacher excites anxieties or fear reflexes. Anxiety and fear never produce a climate in which rational teaching can be achieved.

Is that one of the reasons you have a fund of stories to relate?

Yes, absolutely. Anything that calms the atmosphere is useful.

And do you deliberately distract people if they're getting too intense about things?

Very much so. Because along with wanting to "do" it, people also want to feel it, and to concentrate on it. Most people don't have the concept or experience of inhibition or of leaving themselves alone. In order to get people to leave themselves alone and not to interfere, you distract them. It's quite simple. For instance, if you've got someone standing in front of the chair and you ask them to sit down and say "No" and not give consent and so on, you've already talked about sitting down and they're thinking about sitting down and preparing to do so. But if you say: "Did you see that man who walked past just now?" or just prattle away about something that will tend to distract them, then, when they're distracted and not thinking about it, you can put them into the chair. It's the old, old problem of thinking and feeling: if people are too intent on freeing the neck, sending the head forward and up and so on, they'll get very tied up. I spend a lot of time trying to get people to leave themselves alone. I point out to pupils that they don't want to shorten and pull down and that they should use their full height. But you don't want them to do it. For example, I gave a first lesson to a young woman this morning – she'd had lessons previously from another teacher – and she was going quite well. In the course of the lesson, I said to her that it wasn't necessary for her to think of the head going forward and up, because she'd created a situation in which it was going forward and up. She then told me that in a lesson she didn't like to think of the head going forward and up in any case – she found it all so confusing – and said she found it far better to look out of the window, which, of course, meant she really was leaving herself alone. And she was perfectly right. What she'd been taught previously – or, at any rate, what she'd understood from the teacher – was that the head forward and up was something she had to do and bring about in a direct way, which, of course, is quite wrong.

Essentially, then, people are better off letting you get on with it?

Yes. Having established with a pupil that Alexander lessons are not to be regarded as a treatment and that they've come to learn something, you're often in trouble immediately, because people associate learning with all their old learning habits at school. In fact, you'd be surprised at the number of hang-ups non-academic people have about anything that suggests learning. It triggers off all the old patterns and arouses anxieties: "I mustn't make a fool of myself, I must pay attention, I must be intelligent and try to understand". One often finds this too with older people who've either never had much formal education or been away from the educational process for some time.

As I've indicated, the process of learning the Technique involves three stages: first, people have to be introduced to the experience; secondly, after they've had the experience, the teacher should help them understand what's going on and thus provide an intellectual evaluation or assessment of the situation; thirdly, when the first two stages have been established, the pupil must try to find their own way of applying it and helping themselves. But there are a lot of highly educated and intelligent people who never make it to that point at all. They don't want to and are willing to accept the experience without understanding or applying it. When people don't want to understand or apply it, it's very, very difficult in my experience to do much about it. Many people are afraid it will open up all sorts of things.

Like opening Pandora's box?

Yes. They sense that it's going to open things and so they want to keep well away from it.

And because there is no formal doctrine of change, people have to change – or not – in a way that is relevant or desirable to them, rather than in a way any teacher might have in mind.

That's right. I don't think teachers can change people: the change is up to them. I think if teachers try to make people change they will revolt – eventually. People have various ways of resisting.

So the role of the Alexander teacher is essentially that of a facilitator?

That's really what it is. Moreover, in a situation of this kind, the ordinary stereotype of a teacher doesn't apply at all. It's a learning situation in which both student and teacher are involved. In teaching the Technique, I find that I'm learning from my pupils all the time, and that's what makes the whole thing interesting; otherwise, it would be boring to go through the same old routine day after day, week in and week out. But it's never the same. It's a special type of learning process which makes it different from a school where a teacher has an established body of knowledge to impart and which the pupil is expected to learn. The Technique isn't like that at all; people come to it for practical help in accordance with their needs. It's not good, therefore, for teachers to off-load on to them theoretical considerations – however valid and interesting the teacher finds them – if they're not immediately relevant to the situation.

You mentioned earlier that teachers should treat every lesson as if it were the first lesson, but what do you look for in the course of a lesson – if anything?

I don't have an end in view. Instead, I keep looking to see what's happening or what turns up, and then work accordingly. If someone has a specific difficulty, it's worthwhile discussing the problem. For instance, if someone says: "I find it's difficult to climb the stairs at Holland Park underground station", I say: "Come on, let's see how you climb stairs". I then point out what I observe to be wrong in the way they're tackling it. A common fault in stair-climbing is that people throw the body forward as they approach the stairs, and so when they put the first foot on the stairs, most of their weight is on the leading foot. Then they try to straighten the leg, which leads to all sorts of difficulties. They should try instead to put the leading foot on the stairs with as little weight as they can manage so that the weight is more on the back foot, which enables them to spring off it. Then when they come off the back foot, it's no longer weight-bearing and they can go forward to the next step. And again the weight doesn't come onto it until they've come off the other foot.

Alexander used to recommend walking as a form of "natural" exercise which, as you mentioned earlier, should be performed with mobility and economy of effort. Could you say something about how you approach this subject with pupils?

It depends very much on the individual and what their problems are. But if someone walks badly then I might get on to it quite early. One of the things I then try and find out is whether they've got any preconceived ideas about walking.

You actually ask them to define their beliefs or attitudes?

Not directly. But in the course of conversation it might come up. And, very importantly, when I observe how they walk I can deduce the necessary information. For instance, many people have been told that walking involves throwing the body forward and putting out a foot to stop themselves falling. But I always say, "Well, that's all very well, but as we've only got two legs, walking involves standing on one to move the other. The efficiency with which you move the moveable leg is directly linked to the efficiency with which you stand on the supporting leg." In that way, I get people to think about how to stand on one leg. Once that's established you can then find out what ideas people have about moving or not moving the arms, shoulders and hips. I find that a lot of people think they can move straight forward without any twisting coming into the process. At that point, I try and introduce them to the idea that in pretty much everything we do, there's a element of twist and rotation in the spine which is not only natural but healthy and important. Rotation is associated with a free movement whereas lack of rotation indicates a degree of fixity and rigidity. Moreover, if the joints are loaded so that they're stiff and resistant it will lead to a lot of damage because it overloads the spinal joints. I think it would be true to say that the body weight is always transmitted spirally. Certainly, that was Raymond Dart's opinion and I've never heard anyone contradict his finding regarding the function of the double spiral arrangement of the voluntary musculature.

Now there are any number of errors that people make in walking – they move too quickly, overstride, have the wrong sort of foot contact because they're stiffening the ankles, and interfere with the reflex patterns in the foot, and so on. But is there much point in having a "list" of these faults and then trying to avoid them? Or do you prefer some other way?

I think in walking, like anything else, you want to start by not putting too much demand on – you're not doing it too fast over too great a distance – but the question of balance – the primary control – has got to be the first consideration. You want to ensure that you're not interfering with the head balance and you're keeping your length. Once you've established that, you can try walking a bit faster and a bit more vigorously, watching very closely that there's no stiffening of the neck and head. Matters like length of stride can be assessed experimentally.

Alexander at one stage used to recommend that people take a step backwards before they go into walking. What was the idea there?

It was very much a matter of prevention. People have the habit of throwing the body too far forward at the outset and pulling the head back. Taking a step backwards is an aid to stop this happening.

A lot of running coaches get their charges to monitor the sound of the footfall as a guide to movement efficiency. Would you endorse that?

Yes, that's very useful. FM used to complain about the way people used to walk past his windows, banging the pavement with their feet. He used to say, "As a ratepayer, I ought to sue them!"

I think it would be useful at this point if you could further clarify the relevant difference between thinking and feeling in relation to directing. Perhaps, you could start by explaining from the teacher's point of view what happens when someone tries to feel the direction rather than think it. Is there, for example, a discernible change in the muscle tone?

Yes, very often there is. You feel some sort of tension creeps in. You feel as if the pupil is trying to do something. There's a distinct difference from the teacher's point of view between that feeling and the feeling you get when the pupil really leaves themselves alone. But the easiest way to understand this is to go back to the example of working in front of the mirror. As you direct the mirror image you're not paying attention to the feeling – you're

123

certainly not directing the mirror image by feeling – even though feeling is still there and being registered. When you've gone beyond the mirrors and you understand what you want to happen, you don't look for confirmation that it is happening, but if you get any suspicion that it isn't happening you pay attention at once. The re-education of feeling very much involves it becoming an efficient alarm system rather than a guide. In fact, the analogy of an alarm system isn't a bad one. You wouldn't want an alarm fitted to your car that tells you all the time it wasn't being stolen, would you? You only want to know when it is. It's then that the alarm should sound.

A lot of people worry about the meaning of the directions and try come up with better words or even new directions. Do you think they need to?

No, I don't. If you're directing in front of a mirror you don't really need to pause to think of the words – what you're concerned with is what's taking place in the mirror. And it's only when the mirror is withdrawn or no longer available that you have to direct in the same way as if the mirror were still there. Alexander always used to say it didn't really matter what words you use. You could say, "Jip, jop" if you like. That's why saying the directions like a mantra doesn't work – because the thought isn't there. Alexander didn't regard conscious direction as a conditioning process. Conscious direction to him was something at the very core of the individual and wasn't to be done mechanically any way.

The words or verbal orders, then, are really just pegs on which to hang the sequence of directive thoughts, in your view?

Yes, that's right. But ultimately also the resultant process. It's not just thinking – it's what's actually taking place. It involves the conduction of energy – energy is actually flowing. So we get back to FM's famous definition of direction in *The Use of the Self* where he says:

> When I employ the words "direction" and "directed" with "use" in
> such phrases as "direction of my use" and "I directed the use" etc.,
> I wish to indicate the process involved in projecting messages from
> the brain to the mechanisms and in conducting the energy neces-
> sary to the use of these mechanisms.*

The whole point is that, from a practical point of view, certain
things have got to happen and certain things mustn't happen.
And really it's much more important to see that the wrong thing
doesn't happen than to see that the right thing happens. We're
such creatures of habit that if the wrong thing is allowed to happen, a wrong habit is readily established. People make the mistake of believing that if they carry out an action somehow or another and it's got a lot of mistakes in it, they'll somehow be able to
correct the mistakes later on. But Alexander used to say: "You
never will." So it's important to take things very gradually, step by
step, without any constraint of time. You've got to be prepared to
carry out each bit of the procedure in such a way that the wrong
thing doesn't happen. It might take a lot of time, but really it
takes the time it takes. You're not going to get quicker results at
the expense of making mistakes and getting things wrong, which
is what people are very prone to do. And that, of course, is what
FM meant by "end-gaining".

**Let's be quite clear about this: you're saying, in effect, that even
if you give a pupil or student the relevant experience and get
them to repeat the relevant words or orders at the time of the
experience, then to repeat the words at a later date will not automatically trigger the experience. There has to be something
else, otherwise it's just a mantra?**

That's right. Words can be a reminder and a help in organising
the thinking, but that's all.

**A small minority of people who come for lessons don't seem to
feel very much at all. How do you deal with them?**

---

* F. M. Alexander *The Use of the Self* (1987), p. 35

That's right. They don't. The classic instance of this occurred when I resumed teaching after the war. The pupil, a man, had had three weeks of lessons with another teacher. After one or two lessons with me, I realised that he didn't feel anything at all. So at some point I said to him, "You don't really feel anything, do you?" And he replied, "No, I don't." I went on, "Forgive me for asking this, but I'm curious to know how it is that you've continued with the lessons?" He then said, "Yes, that's a perfectly reasonable question. But the fact of the matter is that after my initial lessons my waistcoat no longer fits and my feet have been affected as well." He was able to deduce a lot of change had taken place, although he couldn't actually feel it. He went on having lessons, and after some time the feeling really did come. And he had an awful time, because what he was feeling was all sorts of soreness, pain and discomfort which he hadn't felt before. The waking up of the feeling was quite an ordeal for him.

So what happens nowadays, if someone tells you they don't feel anything?

I don't take any notice. I just say, "That's okay. Some people don't." You still work on their inhibition and direction and make sure they're leaving themselves alone.

How do you assess the "eye directions" formulated by Kitty Wielopolska (née Merrick)? The claim is that by directing the eyes "free to go apart" and "seeing from the point of vision" some primitive reflex system is activated which facilitates the working of the primary control.*

I think if that were so, then the primary control would no longer be primary. Whatever you're going to do with your eyes – if you're going to look this way or that – you want to ensure as far as you can that you've got the head–neck–back relationship working properly. Then, whatever you think or do with your eyes, you think or

---

* Kitty Wielopolska and M. Pazzaglini "The Discovery and Use of the Eye Order in Teaching the Alexander Technique" (1985).

do it in such a way that you don't interfere with the proper working of the primary control. The important thing is to look outwards and see something and not let the eyes drift off into a haze.

You seem to be saying that keeping the eyes from either becoming "fixed" or "dead" is a useful practice, but that to claim that somehow "eyes free to go apart to see from the point of vision" precedes or is equivalent to the directions for the primary control is a bit far-fetched. Is that so?

Yes. It's not equivalent to the directions relating to the primary control. And personally I don't like giving people instructions that are not practically based. To imagine – as some Alexander teachers tell their pupils – one's eyes resting in their sockets like poached eggs in a cup is a type of imagery that I try to avoid. When I give instructions, I like them to have some objective physiological basis. I don't think, as a matter of fact, that it's possible to move the eyes apart from each other. It may be possible to let the muscles work so that the eyes don't come together or converge quite as much – and that may be a good thing – but the instruction to let the eyes go apart reminds me too much of self-hypnosis. It doesn't appeal to me and it certainly wouldn't have appealed to Alexander. But, on the other hand, he would have agreed that people often make too much effort and create tension in the eyes, so that by deciding to use the eyes differently one can make an improvement.

One must be very careful, however, that people don't run away with the idea that letting the eyes go out of focus is a good thing, because they end up with a non-seeing stare. Alexander considered that a very damaging thing. He used to say that when someone is up and about, they ought to be seeing something. But Kitty might have claimed that by reminding someone to see they can respond by reaching out their eyes on stalks, as it were. It's a complex issue, but let me put it this way: if you said to me, "Look at that plant above the gas fire over there", then my proper procedure would be to say, "No" and then think of my neck being free to allow my head to go forward and up and my eyes to focus on the object quietly until I saw it more clearly.

That's very interesting. It reminds me that pupils sometimes report a shift in their eye level in lessons as a consequence of a change in the head poise. They say things like "I'm looking down at the floor." It's particularly prevalent with pupils who wear glasses.

Yes, it's one of the reasons why FM recommended that people take their glasses off when having a lesson. Apart from anything else it gives the eyes a chance to function without glasses. And certainly people who have a special way of looking through glasses – particularly if they're using bi-focals – often stiffen the neck and pull the head back to do it. That basic misuse will certainly affect the eyes because they're so closely connected to the neck muscles.

From what you've been saying it would seem that you wouldn't encourage visualisation techniques. Is that correct?

No, I wouldn't. If you have any reason to suppose that your neck is stiff, you want to take practical steps to get the neck muscles to release and stretch again. It's a more practical step to allow the weight of the head to tell than to think, for instance, of your head as a balloon. In teaching different people, a teacher might resort to all sorts of experiments, so I wouldn't rule out these things completely. Still, it's a good idea to keep as down to earth and as practical as possible, not least because we're all susceptible to the Walter Mitty syndrome, and it's perfectly possible to walk down the street as heavy as lead whilst blissfully thinking that we're flying like a bird. After all, we have to admit that there are no limits to self-deception. And because self-deception is an ever-present possibility, we must guard against it. Considering all the mistakes we know we make and how wrong we frequently are, it's sensible to do all we can to guard against errors and to acknowledge when we are wrong.

Of course, if you've been working in front of a mirror, then afterwards it's perfectly legitimate to visualise what you've seen in the mirror – you can remember in you mind's eye what it was like – and you can order and direct accordingly. But you still order and direct: you don't try and feel it out. You don't want to get involved in fantasy. Conscious thinking is a rational process. For example, when FM observed in the mirrors that when he went to speak he pulled his head back and depressed his larynx, he reasoned, therefore, that he had to avoid pulling his head back, if he wanted to avoid depressing his larynx. Now, that was a very rational conclusion based on observation.

Now if the basis of the Technique is, as you indicated earlier, "the experience of the experience", what are the implications of this for group work where, for example, there might be one teacher and twenty or thirty people in attendance?

Groups are made up of individuals, and the immediate work has to be addressed to the individual. You can't teach two people simultaneously. But when individuals have had a certain amount of work and experience, and have gained some understanding, then I think group work can be tremendously valuable, because it gives people the opportunity to observe what happens with other people. They can then relate this to their own experience and discuss it with others, which often helps to organise and re-organise their ideas. One also has to bear in mind that in teaching the Technique there's a lot of factual information to be put over, and a group context saves time and trouble. So on a variety of counts group work can be valuable as an introduction.

As far as I can see, group work in the Technique bears a similar relationship to that which ground school in the hangar has to what is taught in the air in flying school. You can't teach two pilots with one set of controls to fly at the same time. Similarly, if an Alexander teacher is confronted with twenty people, he or she should get round and put hands onto everyone to demonstrate the experience. Again, this is the same as learning to fly: the first thing in learning how to fly is to give them air experience – they are flown around and given the opportunity to get the feel of it.

Immediately after this, the group is split into ground school and air school. Ground school is just like any class situation, with a lot of people together. But flying itself has to be done on a one-to-one basis. There's no other way; and it's what makes learning to fly so expensive. At today's levels, it takes something like two million pounds to train a front-line RAF pilot. Obviously, much of that is devoted to the maintenance of the necessary infrastructure, but it's worth pointing out that the whole process culminates in a situation where one man is learning and being taught on a one-to-one basis.

It's undoubtedly true that the Technique has helped many thousands of people. In your experience, however, have there been any individuals or, importantly, categories of individuals who have not been helped by the Technique?

It's difficult to talk about categories because it's such an individual sort of business. A statistician might be able to make sense of it, but I find that it's difficult to predict who will take to it and who won't.

But take someone with a "bad back": have you ever been in a situation where the back hasn't improved?

No, I've never found that to be the case if someone has had as many as thirty lessons. But some people come to the conclusion that they're not going to improve some time before they've had thirty lessons, and drop out. Often this reaction is a subconscious one that has not been thought out or calculated. People are uncertain about getting anywhere, and in this state of uncertainty something crops up; they have to cancel the next lesson, and then never bother to make another appointment.

But a teacher can't have expectations of pupils. It's the old, old story about taking the horse to water; that's all a teacher can do. I'm often sorry and disappointed that somebody doesn't persist, but I know there's rarely anything I can do about it. Sometimes you can sense that somebody is getting depressed and frustrated and feeling that they're not getting anywhere. Then you can perhaps say something to reassure them.

Have you ever thought or said to a pupil that giving them lessons was a complete waste of time?

I've certainly thought it but I don't ever recollect saying it to a pupil. I have, however, managed to work it round so that the pupil has said it to me. And that's the best way! I remember so well a man who came for lessons – this would have been in the 1950s – who was in charge of some large company and reputed to be a mental giant. He came into the teaching-room and said brightly, "You know, I haven't given this a single thought since I was here last time." Now, that was a complete waste of time. Very definitely. And then there was the remarkable man who came for lessons at the same time as he had some important business to complete over the following months. My response to him was, "Well, we'll give it a try, and see what happens." I found out that he'd started off as a barrister, changed to a solicitor, before becoming involved in high finance in the City and a Fellow of All Souls. When we got to work, I'd never met anyone whose neck was so stiff – it was impossible to get any movement at all – and after a week or two of lessons he said to me, "Isn't it a pity that your Technique calls for people to free their necks, because if what was required was stiffening of the neck, I'd be your star pupil, wouldn't I?" So in a sort of desperation I said to him, "Well, go on. Stiffen your neck, and see how really stiff you can make it." Whereupon it became perfectly free. Of course, I was surprised, but he was absolutely shattered! So we discussed the matter and I said, "Now, what you've got to do is take a holiday and you've got to be prepared to come to me every day for three weeks and do absolutely nothing else." He said that he would have to think it over – this was on the Tuesday – and the following Monday I got a note from him saying he'd thought it over and was sure that my advice was quite right, but that in present circumstances there was no way he could take a break, but if at some point in the future he could manage it, he would. But I never saw him again.

So that was that. In fact, I heard from someone else that he'd died a short time later.

What do you think are the main limitations of the Technique?

It depends what you mean by limitations. The Technique deals with only a relatively small part of the process of living, albeit an important part, as FM made clear in his first book, *Man's Supreme Inheritance,* when he stated that the Technique doesn't prophesy "unlimited sunshine for everyone, without regard to conditions" and it isn't a "royal road" or "panacea".* As I've said before, there are many other things in life besides the Alexander Technique and people with problems need all the help they can get. Yet the Technique has a contribution to make to most things, because the practical concepts of "end-gaining" and "means whereby", are universally applicable. Most things can be tackled consciously and rationally.

But the rational and conscious make up only a very small part of reality and we must, therefore, make a generous allowance for what isn't accessible to consciousness and rationality. This is important, and we certainly shouldn't pretend that it doesn't exist. In fact, the perspective that consciousness affords is limited and rationality only works in certain areas. As you know, much progress is made by intuition and processes other than conscious ones.

Intuition, for example, is mysterious: feelings of all grades come into it as well as thoughts, ideas and beliefs, and there are undoubtedly people who are highly intuitive. Lots of inventors, innovators and creative artists claim that their achievements are not due to rationality or consciousness at all. But, as Alexander would have said: "That's all right as far as it goes, but it's certainly not reliable and how far can you trust it?" The assumption underlying the Technique is that rationality is worth pursuing. After all, as we noted earlier, Alexander referred to the "supreme inheritance of a conscious mind".

---

* F. M. Alexander *Man's Supreme Inheritance* (1996) p. xix.

Marjorie Barstow in her preface to *The Use of the Self* stated: "I have heard people say that the Technique is difficult. The longer I work with the Technique, the more I realise how simple it actually is."* Has that been your experience – but does it take time to appreciate the simplicity and depth in teaching the Technique?

Yes. It takes a long time to understand what the Technique is about – never mind whether it's simple or complex.

But that acknowledgement goes against the grain of modern society, where instant or, at least, near-instant solutions are demanded.

That's very true, and it is the difficulty, of course. It does take time. And for the reasons that FM claimed: everyone thinks in terms of separation of mind and body, and even when they claim to think holistically they don't really do so. The other difficulty is that people tend to think in the abstract and the thought process – the reasoning process – is widely understood in those terms.

So how long did it take things to fall into place for you?

Oh, a very long time. It's a slow, gradual process. I was beginning to grasp some of the concepts after I'd been qualified some twenty years.

It might be said that you were taking a lot on faith?

You could say I was taking it on faith in a way, but I was talking about grasping the concepts. I'd learned the practical procedures on the training course, so taking someone in and out of the chair, for example, wasn't unfamiliar or taken on faith, because the procedures confirm their validity every time you carry them out. But to be able to explain to yourself what's going on – let alone why, to anybody else – is a different matter. There are excellent Alexander teachers – indeed, there always have been – who probably

---

* Marjorie Barstow in F. M. Alexander *The Use Of The Self* (1984).

can't explain it, even though they can give an excellent experience with their hands. But many people nowadays do their three years training and go out and start teaching and are doing very well. They're helping people almost straightaway, and by the time they have two or three years experience, one might regard them as good teachers. What I'm saying is that the quality of training improves all the time, so it's always to be expected or, at least, hoped that the latest people to qualify will be rather better equipped than their predecessors were to learn and develop from their subsequent experience.

But overall patience is of the essence?

I don't see how it can be hurried. FM always used to compare the Technique to gardening, which is a good analogy. There are no satisfactory shortcuts in gardening and it's the same with the Technique. I would say though that a good dose of manure can work wonders.

Ah, but where does one get the manure from?

Some people seem to generate it more than others. But seriously, one has to allow oneself to be taught. I think that's really the trick. That's what FM maintained too. He used to say: "The greatest difficulty the teacher has is to get the pupil to allow him or herself to be taught."

So one needs what – humility?

No, I don't think pride is the stumbling block. It's more to do with misconception and misunderstanding. A lot of it, as I mentioned earlier, is tied up with our previous experiences in education and the posture one feels one has to adopt if one is to learn.

Walter, I started this discussion by asking what motivated you to train in the Technique, so it seems appropriate to close it by asking what motivates you now?

I find it even more interesting and fascinating the longer I go on working at it. I get new experiences and new insights all the time.

It really is extremely enjoyable.

And if you had your time again I assume that you wouldn't have chosen to be a solicitor or a chartered accountant, rather than an Alexander teacher?

Certainly not. No, I'm very glad indeed that I did what I did. I wouldn't want to have done anything else.

Appendix

Diary of First Lessons with Alexander

November 25th 1935, Monday

I had my first lesson from Mr Alexander today. He dealt with the underlying general principles of relaxation, i.e., as Jacobson points out, just not-contracting. He manipulated the head by (it seems), putting his fingers on the junction of the head and neck at the base of the skull with thumbs under the jaw-bone. Direction for the neck to relax and the head to go forward and up was then given. He straightened the alignment of head and neck with his fingers and pulled the head upwards. His secret is re-coordinating the organism so as to create fresh behaviour patterns. He suggested that we today live by calculating people's reactions to stimuli, and so by presentation of stimuli, forming their behaviour to our own ends. This is probably highly immoral: what we should seek to do is free them from these automatic reactions. The first step in such a process is clearly immediate inhibition on presentation of a stimulus.

November 26, Tuesday

Tonight I encountered much greater difficulty. It's no use taking this business seriously and concentrating on it. The directions have got to be subvocalized all the time. The process is rather like that of a juggler just keeping things going. In sitting down or standing up, for instance, the direction must be given and the knees allowed to go forward and out. Once you start thinking about the process it is no good. I notice also that while the directions are going there is a distinct feeling at the base of the neck and across the back. When you come to think of it, it does not say much for man as a civilized and rational animal that we have to spend so much time and effort in calculating his reactions to any situation. Man ought to have learnt to react consciously and intelligently by this time. I observe that it is most difficult to get the directions started first thing in the morning. A little meditation is required before the head will go forward and up.

November 27 and 28, Wednesday & Thursday

Yesterday I was very struck with what might be regarded as the philosophical aspect of this work. Alexander says that improperly co-ordinated people cannot think and that their judgement is valueless. But then, after all, how does he know what constitutes co-ordination? May not these people be right and he wrong? If people have to be properly co-ordinated before they can think, will they have any time left for thinking after co-ordination? Dewey is only a second-class mind. Surely the sane view is that people can and do do things in spite of handicaps and deformities. We must not condemn the work of all mal-coordinated people because they are mal-coordinated: that savours too much of religion! Also it is well that brother ass should be well tended and groomed; but he is there for us to ride on and we must ride sometimes.

To return to practicalities. Following out my idea (above) I succeeded well yesterday by keeping up a fairly lively conversation while he was manipulating. This just gave the right amount of concentration. He took me in the chair and used the "book" a little.

Today I seemed to be making good progress. The sensations of stiffness in the back and neck were quite normal and due to bringing a new set of muscles into play. Also, they were probably due to getting the chin so far downwards with the result of stiffening the neck. As Alexander continually repeats "it is the means whereby (ugly phrase) that matters". When I want the salt at table I don't have to think how I am to get it, I just reach out and there it is! Similarly if I leave my head and neck to relax and go forward and up by themselves, they will do so. I have no need to picture "forward and up" to myself. I already know what that means. If I try to "put" the head I shall, of course, stiffen the neck. In this stage Alexander is really recording new sensations for the kinaesthetic sense. Any stiffness or failure to keep the directions going just scratches the photographic plate. He is responsible for all movements and adjustments, one just leaves the field free for him.

November 29, Friday

I am just beginning to understand the importance of inhibition. It is not sufficient just to release the neck and let the head forward and up, the least thought of purpose of an action, e.g. to sit down or to bend, causes a stiffening. At this stage I have not only to give the directions but positively to insist over and over again that "I am not going to do so and so". You have to make up your mind not to do the thing and then you can do it! Inhibition is the most important lesson in the whole Technique. Today I was taken as usual in the chair and then standing and with the arms on the chair in front. Then rising onto the toes in this position. But I will not inhibit. However, I managed all right in the end. It appears that I am not likely to have great difficulty once I learn to inhibit.

November 30, Saturday

There is surprisingly little to add about today. Things seemed to go very well. He took me standing up with my knees bent forward and trunk leaning forward. Then by lengthening and widening and coming back to his hand in the small of my back I was supposed to rise on my toes. Sorry to say that I did not inhibit properly so it did not work. However it was a good lesson in the end.

December 2, Monday

Again a successful but otherwise uneventful lesson. I had surmounted yesterday's difficulties. He made me move my head from side to side without moving my shoulders. I managed this quite successfully. Tomorrow is the performance (Rudolf Steiner Hall; K) so I don't go again until . . .

December 4, Wednesday

Tonight I have to record by far the worst lesson that I have had so far. I just seemed incapable of releasing the neck in doing the hands on chair business. This inability is humiliating to a degree beyond fury. As soon as he touches me I seem to stiffen by reflex action: I came away from the lesson with an enormous degree of irritation and depression. It has taken me nearly two hours to get back to normal. Of course I recognize the subconscious reason for it: I have been trying from the first to create an impression on the man and I can draw nothing from him. It is my self-esteem – no small thing – that is hurt. And does it infuriate! However this is a state of mind incompatible with the notions of the Technique and it will depart in time. It is all this damned earnestness. I must take care to inhibit in the predominantly mental sphere as well as in the predominantly physical. The point is that it is really necessary to meditate – to think carefully – about the Technique. I must try this and see what happens tomorrow.

December 5, Thursday

My analysis was apparently quite correct for I had an extremely good lesson tonight. By talking all the time I must have kept the right amount of inhibition going. Talking of Aldous Huxley, he said that such a man might as easily have discovered the Technique as himself. The whole business depends so much on thought and attitude of mind. In some people what Alexander pleases to call conscientiousness takes the form of muscular tensions. This is a great misfortune and a state of affairs to be amended. Perhaps I am coming to be too dependent on my own ideas. I must learn to use and react to those of other people. The mental attitude is the secret of the Technique.

December 6, Friday

Today, through a mistake Mr Alexander was unable to take me

and Miss Webb took me instead. She gave me a most interesting lesson in front of the mirrors and I was able to see my head and observe the appearance of my neck when relaxed and stiffened.

December 7, Saturday

I had a very bad lesson. My neck was very stiff. It was a beastly morning and I was not in a very bright temper. Alexander nagged until I began to stiffen every time he approached me.

December 9, Monday

I really began to see light over the weekend. The grand conception of the work has come home to me. I understand that really the "means justifies the end"; that until we have physically experienced the process of inhibition and making conscious adjustments in small things, we cannot do so in big things. It is no use appealing to sensation for guidance. Whatever message the senses give, the opposite is probably true. If a person undertakes to perform a physical act correctly, you can be sure that they cannot do so; for the last thing they will try is the way that feels the wrong way and that alone will be right. Alexander is engaged in freeing us from the spectre of teleology. Life to him is a real dance and it is the mode of dancing that matters not the distance in any direction that one steps over.

December 10, Tuesday

Another very good lesson. I chatted away about trivialities and all went splendidly. There is a great difference between intellectual assent to a proposition and physical assent. It is for that reason that Alexander must concentrate on the physical aspect first. Inhibition must be practised physically before it can be experienced mentally. *A fortiori*, it must be lived physically before it can be lived mentally. It is a favourite dictum of his that anything that can be finished is not worth doing at all. By this he means that it is always the activity that matters and not the end. Physically and mentally we always tend to end-gain unless we inhibit.

December 11, Wednesday, 12 Thursday, 13 Friday and 16 Monday

These were all very successful lessons and the improvement seems to be permanent. A number of new notions have occurred about the Technique although I have been taken in no new positions or had any difficulties. I have decided to present copies of FM's works to Campion Hall and Heythrop before I join the Society. Alexander gains a great deal by having no name or label for his technique. All labels would be a misrepresentation and without them all except reasoned critics, if there are any such, are confounded. We are all familiar with the theory about the decay that sets in in civilized and prosperous nations after a number of years: is this not caused by the fact that under any civilization the new adjustments demanded by the environment increase in number and complexity all the time until the mechanisms of sensory perception completely break down? Most of us suffer from that frightful disease, lack of confidence in ourselves: is it not a frightful thing that we have to wonder about our power to remember things, to follow out our best judgements and so on? Surely this condition that we are in, that will not even enable us to stop doing things against our will, is a terrible thing. It is bringing us all to the state when we shall be mere puppets of whoever would control us to his own ends. Let us learn not to do things anyway even if we can't learn to do them. FM says that given thirty good teachers and a supply of normal children they could train several thousand a year. With a normal child only a few weeks in small classes is necessary. That is why we must concentrate on the schools and education. FM also says that even after all these years he is not sure that his sensory mechanism approximates sufficiently to normality for him to trust himself to sit on a jury. Thus the process of education always goes on and is never finished.

About the authors

Walter Carrington trained with F. Matthias Alexander from 1936 to 1939. From 1941 to 1946 he served as a pilot in the Royal Air Force. He worked at Alexander's teachers' training course 1946–55 and continued running the training course after Alexander's death at the Constructive Teaching Centre in London of which he is the director. He has given workshops internationally for teachers, and has lectured and written extensively on the Technique. Among his published works are *The Foundations of Human Well-Being*, *Explaining the Alexander Technique* (with Seán Carey), *Thinking Aloud* (ed. J. Sontag), *The Act of Living* (ed. J. Sontag) and *A Time to Remember*. He is a member and past chairman of the Society of Teachers of the Alexander Technique.

Seán Carey gained a Ph. D. in social anthropology at the University of Newcastle-upon-Tyne. He trained at Alexander Teaching Associates in London from 1982 to 1985. He has a full-time teaching practice in London and in Hertfordshire. He is also the co-author of *Explaining the Alexander Technique* (with Walter Carrington) and *The Alexander Technique* (with John Nicholls). He is a member of the Society of Teachers of the Alexander Technique.

Bibliography

Alexander, F. Matthias *Man's Supreme Inheritance* (Mouritz, London, 1996)

Alexander, F. Matthias *The Use of the Self* (Centerline Press, California, 1984)

Alexander, F. Matthias *The Use of the Self* (Gollancz, London, 1987)

Barlow, Wilfred *The Alexander Principle* (Arrow, London, 1975)

Carrington, Walter H. M. *F. M. Alexander – Part I, II and III narrated by Walter H. M. Carrington* (The Constructive Teaching Centre Ltd., London, 1992)

Carrington, Walter H. M. *The Foundations of Human Well-Being* (STAT Books, London, 1994)

Dart, Raymond A. *Skill and Poise* (STAT Books, London, 1996)

Feldenkrais, Moshe *Body and Mature Behaviour – A study of Anxiety, Sex, Gravitation and Learning* (Routledge & Kegan Paul, London, 1949).

Gorman, John *The Cause of Lumbar Back Pain and the Solution* (Published by the author, Basingstoke, 1983)

Heggie, Jack *Running with the Whole Body* (Rodale Press, Pennsylvania, 1986)

Jones, Frank Pierce *Freedom to Change* (Mouritz, London, 1997)

Libet, Benjamin "Unconscious cerebral initiative and the role of conscious will in voluntary action" in *The Behavioural and Brain Sciences*, 1985, 8, 529.

Westfeldt, Lulie *F. Matthias Alexander: The Man and His Work* (Mouritz, London, 1998)

Wielopolska, Kitty and M. Pazzaglini "The Discovery and Use of the Eye Order in Teaching the Alexander Technique", edited by Carol A. Attwood (photocopy, 1985).

Index